Popular Complete Smart Series

• Advanced •
Complete
MathSmart®
Grade 8

Proud Sponsor of the Math Team of Canada 2017

ISBN: 978-1-77149-206-5

ISBN: 978-1-77149-206-5

A Message to Parents

Advanced Complete MathSmart is an extension of our bestselling *Complete MathSmart* series. This series focuses on challenging word problems that require the application of the math concepts and skills that children have learned in the *Complete MathSmart* series.

The two sections in this book are designed to gradually develop your child's problem-solving and critical-thinking skills. In Section 1, each unit covers one core topic and begins with basic skills questions, followed by problem-solving questions that increase in difficulty as the unit progresses. It reinforces your child's math concepts and skills in the topic in focus. Working through this section, your child should be able to proficiently explain and illustrate the solutions to the word problems.

Section 2 provides abundant critical-thinking questions, each combining multiple topics from Section 1. The topics are integrated in different ways to provide a wide range of complex and challenging questions that help stimulate your child's mathematical reasoning and develop his or her critical-thinking skills.

An answer key with step-by-step solutions is also provided at the end of this comprehensive book. All the solutions are presented in a clear and organized way to allow your child to have a thorough understanding of the math concepts.

Advanced Complete MathSmart will not only improve your child's core math understanding and skills, but also develop his or her critical-thinking skills which are essential in solving daily life challenges.

Your Partner in Education,
Popular Book Co. (Canada) Ltd.

ISBN: 978-1-77149-206-5

Advanced Complete MathSmart

Section 1:
Basic Problem-solving Questions

ISBN: 978-1-77149-206-5

Contents

Section 2:
Critical-thinking Questions

Level 1 – with hints

Level 2 – without hints

 ISBN: 978-1-77149-206-5

ISBN: 978-1-77149-206-5

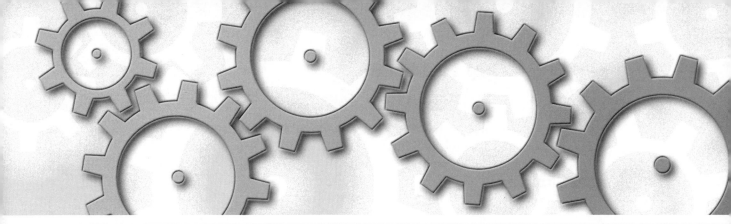

Section 1:
Basic Problem-solving
Questions

ISBN: 978-1-77149-206-5

Real Numbers

solving a variety of word problems that involve integers, exponents, square roots, and scientific notation

 Math Skills

Integers

① $(-2) + 4$ = __2__ ② $3 - (-1)$ = __4__ ③ $(-2) \times (-3)$ = __6__

④ $(-9) \div 3$ = __-3__ ⑤ $4 \times (-2)$ = __-8__ ⑥ $(-12) \div (-2)$ = __6__

Exponents

⑦ $3^2 \times 3^4 = 3^{2+4} = 3^6 =$ __729__   ⑧ $4^3 \times 4^2 =$ __4^5__ = ___ = ___

⑨ $6^3 \div 6^2 =$ __6^{3-2}__ $= 6^1 = 6$ ⑩ $2^{10} \div 2^{10} = 2^{10-10} = 2^0 = 1$

Squares and Square Roots

⑪ $\sqrt{9 \times 4}$
$= \sqrt{9} \times \sqrt{4}$
$= 3 \times 2$
$= 6$

⑫ $\sqrt{\frac{4}{9}}$ $\frac{\sqrt{4}}{\sqrt{9}}$ $\frac{4}{9}$
$= \frac{\sqrt{4}}{\sqrt{9}}$
$= \frac{2}{3}$

⑬ $\sqrt{16 \times 25}$
$= \sqrt{16} \times \sqrt{25}$
$= 4 \times 5$
$= 20$

⑭ $\sqrt{\frac{16}{25}}$
$= \frac{\sqrt{16}}{\sqrt{25}}$
$= \frac{4}{5}$

⑮ $(2^8 \div 2^6 + 3^1 \times 3^2)$

$(2^2) + (3^3)$

$4 + 27 = 31$

⑯ $5^2 \div (\sqrt{9} + \sqrt{4})$

$5^2 \div (\sqrt[3]{9} + \sqrt[2]{4})$

$25 \div (5)$

$= 5$

⑰ $\sqrt{9^{-1} \times 3^2}$

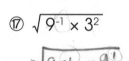
$\sqrt{9^{-1} \times 9^0}$

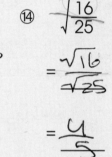
$\sqrt{9^0}$

$\sqrt{1} = 1$

⑱ $\dfrac{2^4 \times 3^7 \times 5^3}{3^8 \times 2^3 \times 5^4}$

⑲ $(-2 + 8)^3 \div 6^2$

⑳ $\dfrac{2^2 - 3^2 + 1^3}{(-4)^2 \div (-2)^3}$

 ISBN: 978-1-77149-206-5

Problem Solving

$\sqrt{9} = 3$

$\sqrt{} = 4$ $\sqrt{-9'} = \sqrt{9^{-1}}$

$\sqrt{16}$

$(-2) + (-6) \times 3$

Try This!

A game has four rounds. Jordan got -2 points in one round and -6 points in three rounds. How many points did he get in all?

$(-2) + (-6) \times 3$

Solution:

Step 1: **Write a number sentence.**

$(-2) + (-6) \times 3 = \boxed{-20}$

$(-2) + -18$

> Remember these rules for operations with negative numbers.

Step 2: **Evaluate.**

$(-2) + (-6) \times 3$

$= (-2) + \boxed{-18}$ ← Multiplying a negative no. by a positive no. results in a negative no.

$= (-2) - \boxed{}$ ← Adding a negative no. implies subtraction.

$= \boxed{}$

Operations	
Addition	**Subtraction**
+ + ➤ +	− + ➤ −
+ − ➤ −	− − ➤ +
Multiplication	**Division**
(+) × (+) ➤ +	(+) ÷ (+) ➤ +
(+) × (−) ➤ −	(+) ÷ (−) ➤ −
(−) × (+) ➤ −	(−) ÷ (+) ➤ −
(−) × (−) ➤ +	(−) ÷ (−) ➤ +

Step 3: **Write a concluding sentence.**

Jordan got $\boxed{}$ points in all.

$9^a \times 9^b$ 9^{a+b}

① Refer to the question above.

  a. Sam got -10 points in two rounds and 4 points in the other two rounds. How many points did he get?

$(-10) \times 2 + 4 \times 2$

$21^1 \times 21^3$ 21^{1+3} 21^4

Sam got ___-12___ points.

  b. Who, Jordan or Sam, got a greater mean score? By how many points?

_____ got a greater mean score by _____ points.

* "mean" = sum ÷ count (average)

② I recorded last week's temperatures in this table.

a. What was the mean temperature last week?

The mean temperature last week was
__-1__ °C.

Temperatures Last Week

Day	Temperature
Mon	-8°C
Tue	-3°C
Wed	0°C
Thu	-2°C
Fri	8°C

b. The mean temperature next week is expected to be 5°C cooler than twice the mean temperature of last week. What is the expected mean temperature?

The expected mean temperature is __-7__ °C.

③ There are 3 numbered cards as shown. A player draws two cards without replacement and multiplies the numbers.

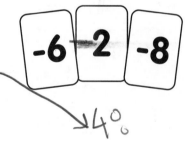

a. What is the difference between the greatest product and the least product?

48

- 16

The difference is __64__ .

b. If the sign of the number on one of the cards is changed so that all products are positive integers, what is the change? Explain.

_____

_____

_____

  ISBN: 978-1-77149-206-5

④ A box has 5^2 nails. How many nails are there in 5^3 boxes?

There are __5^5__ (3125) nails.

⑤ There are 4^5 students at an elementary school. If 4^7 pencils are evenly distributed among the students, how many pencils does each student get?

Each student gets __16__ pencils.

⑥ Asher's farm has 3^4 chickens. Each chicken lays 3^5 eggs at most in a year.

a. How many eggs will the chickens lay at most in a year?

$(3 \times 3 \times 3 \times 3 \times 3 \times 3 \times 3 \times 3 \times 3) \times 3$

1yr

The chickens will lay __3^9__ eggs at most in a year.

b.

How many eggs will they lay at most in 3 years?

Write the answer as an exponent.

$\times 3$

Asher

The chickens will lay __3^{10}__ eggs at most in 3 years.

⑦ The populations of Quebec and Nunavut in 2016 are about 2^{23} and 2^{15} people respectively. How many times larger is Quebec's population than Nunavut's?

_____

⑧ How many $100 bills are needed to make $10 million?

_____

⑨ Brian follows a pattern to make triangles as shown. He shows the number of sticks used in each frame in the table.

a. Brian takes all the sticks used for Frame 4 to build Frame 3. How many of Frame 3 can he build?

Number of Sticks used in Frames

Frame No.	No. of Sticks
1	3^1
2	3^2
3	3^3
4	3^4

_____

b. Brian takes apart 3 Frame 3's and uses all the sticks to build Frame 2. How many of Frame 2 can he build?

Frame 1

Frame 2

Frame 3

Frame 4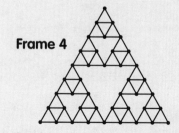

_____

ISBN: 978-1-77149-206-5

⑩ Jack has garden tiles that make 2 squares with side lengths of 4 m and 3 m. He wants to rearrange all the garden tiles and combine them to make 1 big square.

a. What will the side length of the big square be?

_____

b. If each tile has a side length of 0.2 m, how many tiles are there?

_____

⑪ The floor plan of Eliza's home is shown. The garage is next to 2 square rooms. What is the area of the garage?

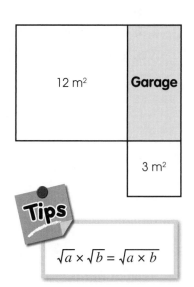

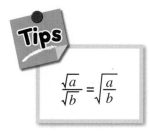

_____

⑫ Maverick has 2 square pictures with areas of 400 cm² and 100 cm². How many times larger is the side length of the big picture than that of the small picture?

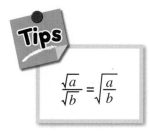

_____

ISBN: 978-1-77149-206-5

⑬ A watermelon seed weighs 10^{-1} g and a watermelon can grow up to 10^4 g. How many times bigger can a watermelon be than its seed?

_____

⑭ A honeybee is 5^{-3} m long but can travel 5^8 times its body length to forage for food. How far can a honeybee travel? Give the answer as an exponent.

_____

⑮ In Lake Ontario, there are approximately 2.5×10^{-11} plankton in every litre of water. How many plankton are there in Lake Ontario if it has 1.64×10^{15} L of water? Write your answer in scientific notation.

Tips

Scientific notation is a way to write very large or very small numbers.

the decimal point moved 5 places to the left

e.g. $1\underset{5\ 4\ 3\ 2\ 1}{20000.} = \boxed{1.2} \times \boxed{10^5}$

between 1 and 10   power of 10

_____

⑯

In 2013, 1.5×10^7 tourists visited Canada.

Answer the questions below in scientific notation.

a. What was the mean number of visitors in a month?

_____

b. On average, every tourist contributed $\$1.16 \times 10^3$ to the tourism industry. How much did the tourists contribute in 2013?

_____

ISBN: 978-1-77149-206-5

⑰ A square park has side lengths of 11^2 m. A rectangular park has an area of 11^3 m². Which park has a greater area? By how many times?

_____

⑱ Determine whether each child is correct or incorrect.

a. Kyle said, "$(-3)^2$ is the same as -3^2."

_____

b. William said, "$(\sqrt{25})^2$ equals 25."

_____

c. Sandra said, "6^2 is the same as $(-6)^2$."

_____

d. Alfred said, "$\sqrt{9^2}$ is the same as 9."

_____

ISBN: 978-1-77149-206-5

Fractions and Decimals

solving a variety of word problems that involve fractions, decimals, and the conversion between the two

 Math Skills

① $\dfrac{1}{7} \times \dfrac{3}{4} = \dfrac{3}{28}$

② $\dfrac{5}{9} \times \dfrac{23}{3} = \dfrac{15}{18}$

③ $1\dfrac{2}{5} \times \dfrac{1}{4} = \dfrac{7}{20}$

④ $2\dfrac{5}{6} \div 1\dfrac{1}{3} = \dfrac{51}{24}$

⑤ $2\dfrac{1}{6} + 4\dfrac{1}{5} \div \dfrac{27}{15} = $ _____

⑥ $\dfrac{11}{7} \times 3\dfrac{1}{2} + 9\dfrac{2}{3} \div 7\dfrac{1}{4} = $ _____

⑦ $1\dfrac{2}{3} + 6\dfrac{2}{5} \times \dfrac{5}{8} - \dfrac{11}{2} = $ _____

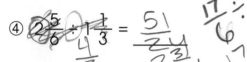

⑧ $12.5 \times 3.5 = $ _____

⑨ $15.75 \div 0.25 = $ _____

⑩ $0.0024 \times 50 = $ _____

⑪ $3.48 \div 24 = $ _____

⑫ $0.125 \times 1.88 = $ _____

⑬ $2.685 \div 0.075 = $ _____

⑭ $(0.25 + 0.8) \times 1.3 = $ _____

⑮ $6.8 \div 2 + 0.9 \times 3 = $ _____

⑯ $1.5 + 1.4 \div 0.07 - 9.76 = $ _____

Fraction	Decimal
$\dfrac{1}{4}$	= _____
_____	= 0.4
$\dfrac{3}{8}$	= _____
_____	= 1.2
$1\dfrac{3}{4}$	= _____
_____	= 3.5
$2\dfrac{4}{5}$	= _____

Convert the numbers in bold by referring to the chart.

⑰ $0.8 + 1.2 \times \dfrac{\mathbf{1}}{\mathbf{4}}$ $= 0.8 + 1.2 \times$ _____ = _____

⑱ $\dfrac{3}{5} \div (\dfrac{1}{2} + \mathbf{0.4}) = $ _____ = _____

⑲ $1.8 \div \dfrac{\mathbf{3}}{\mathbf{8}} - 1.03 = $ _____ = _____

⑳ $\mathbf{1.2} + 1\dfrac{5}{6} \times 2\dfrac{1}{4} = $ _____ = _____

㉑ $10.2 - \mathbf{1\dfrac{3}{4}} \times 2.1 = $ _____ = _____

㉒ $2\dfrac{1}{2} \times \dfrac{6}{7} + \mathbf{3.5} \times 1\dfrac{1}{7} = $ _____ = _____

㉓ $\mathbf{2\dfrac{4}{5}} \div 0.4 - 2.6 \div 1.3 = $ _____ = _____

ISBN: 978-1-77149-206-5

Problem Solving

> I completed an obstacle course in $6\frac{2}{3}$ min. It took Greg $1\frac{1}{2}$ times as long to complete it.

Gary

Greg

How much faster was Gary than Greg in minutes?

Solution:

Step 1: Write a number sentence.

$$6\frac{2}{3} \times 1\frac{1}{2} - 6\frac{2}{3} = \boxed{}$$

Step 2: Evaluate.

$$6\frac{2}{3} \times 1\frac{1}{2} - 6\frac{2}{3}$$

$$= \boxed{} \times \boxed{} - 6\frac{2}{3}$$

$$= \boxed{} - 6\frac{2}{3}$$

$$= \boxed{}$$

Step 3: Write a concluding sentence.

Gary was $\boxed{}$ min

faster than Greg.

① Refer to the question above. It took George $\frac{3}{4}$ of the time Gary needed to complete the obstacle course. How much faster was George than Gary in minutes?

George was _____ min faster than Gary.

ISBN: 978-1-77149-206-5

② Milo observed that a Ferris wheel revolves $4\frac{4}{5}$ times in $2\frac{1}{4}$ minutes. How many times does the Ferris wheel revolve in 10 minutes?

The Ferris wheel revolves _____ times in 10 minutes.

③ Carla baked an apple pie. She ate $\frac{1}{10}$ of it and each of her 6 friends ate $\frac{1}{8}$ of it. How much of the pie remains?

_____ of the pie remains.

④ Michael completed 4 chores in 2 h. One of the chores took him $\frac{3}{5}$ h and two of the other chores each took him $\frac{2}{3}$ h. How long did the remaining chore take him?

The remaining chore took him _____ h.

⑤ A jug has $3\frac{1}{3}$ L of water after $\frac{1}{6}$ of it was poured out. How much water was poured out in litres?

_____ L of water was poured out.

ISBN: 978-1-77149-206-5

⑥ Sammy and Diana were playing basketball. They each made 20 throws. Sammy scored $\frac{2}{5}$ of his total throws and Diana scored $\frac{3}{10}$ of hers.

> How many more throws did I score than Diana?

Sammy

Sammy scored _____ more throws.

⑦ Melanie put $1\frac{1}{2}$ bags of peanuts into a jar. She then used $\frac{1}{6}$ of the peanuts in the jar. If each bag had $\frac{4}{5}$ kg of peanuts, how many kilograms of peanuts are left in the jar?

_____ kg of peanuts are left.

⑧ Arnold lives $8\frac{1}{2}$ km away from a theatre. To get to the theatre, Arnold walks $\frac{1}{10}$ of the distance to a bus stop and then travels by bus.

a. If the bus makes a stop every $\frac{17}{20}$ km, how many stops will the bus make after Arnold gets on it?

The bus will make _____ stops.

b. There is a library at the 4th bus stop. How far is the library from Arnold's house?

The library is _____ km from Arnold's house.

ISBN: 978-1-77149-206-5

⑨

> My favourite band has released a new album available for download. Each track costs $0.99 and there are 12 tracks in all.

Alternatively, it costs $10.99 to download the entire album. How much more does it cost to download all the tracks individually?

_____

⑩ A medical test has an accuracy rate of 0.95. If 60 tests are done, how many test results are inaccurate?

_____

⑪ Justin drinks 0.25 L of milk every day. He plans to increase his consumption by 0.1 L each day. How many days will it take Justin to finish 4.2 L of milk?

_____

⑫ Almonds are sold by weight. During a sale event, the cost of 1 kg of almonds was decreased from $17.60 to $12.35. Mr. Sun bought 2.8 kg of almonds. How much did he save?

_____

ISBN: 978-1-77149-206-5

⑬ Timothy ate 0.1 of 2.68 kg of snacks. He then divided the remaining snacks equally into 4 bags. How many kilograms of snacks were there in each bag?

_____

⑭ There are 5 rolls of ribbon. 4 of the rolls are each 5.5 m long and the remaining roll is 1.25 m longer. What is the total length of the ribbon?

_____

⑮ A 0.75-L bottle of shampoo costs $5.25. Its value size has 0.45 L more shampoo and it costs $2.19 more than the regular size.

a. How much does 1 L of shampoo in value size cost?

_____

b.

I want to buy 6 L of shampoo. How much will I save if I buy in value size?

 ISBN: 978-1-77149-206-5

⑯ It cost Janet $51.78 to fill $\frac{3}{4}$ of her car's gas tank. How much would it have cost to fill up the gas tank?

_____

⑰ Louis is trying to sell the remaining pizzas at the end of the day. He is selling $\frac{2}{3}$ of a cheese pizza for $5.50 and $\frac{5}{8}$ of a pepperoni pizza for $4.55. Which pizza is a better deal?

_____

⑱ The regular cost of 1 kg of beans is $6.33. Sandra has a coupon that reduces the cost by half. How much will $\frac{1}{4}$ kg of beans cost?

_____

⑲ Keith paid 3 quarters to park his car for $\frac{1}{4}$ h. How much would it have cost to park the car for $1\frac{1}{2}$ h?

_____

⑳

I mixed $\frac{7}{8}$ of this bottle of soda with $\frac{3}{5}$ of this carton of juice to make fruit punch.

Jason

Soda 2.64 L

Juice 1.32 L

How much fruit punch did Jason make?

_____

ISBN: 978-1-77149-206-5

㉑ Mr. Arnold is making concrete by mixing 1.15 kg of water with $2\frac{4}{5}$ kg of cement mix. The concrete is enough to fill $1\frac{2}{3}$ holes. How much concrete is there in 1 hole?

㉒ 0.84 L of tomato sauce fills $1\frac{2}{5}$ containers. How much tomato sauce should Dino make to fill $2\frac{4}{5}$ containers?

㉓ Sandy and Connie split the cost of their meal. Sandy paid $12.75, which was $\frac{1}{3}$ of the bill. Connie paid the remaining with a $50 bill. What was Connie's change?

㉔ $\frac{1}{5}$ of a rope was 8.25 m long. Albert used 2.5 m of the rope. What is the mass of the remaining rope if each metre weighs 0.4 kg?

㉕ The cost of an apple is $\frac{3}{4}$ of the cost of a pear. If a pear costs $2.40, how many apples can be bought with the money needed for 3 pears?

ISBN: 978-1-77149-206-5

show $\frac{1}{5}$ as %; decimal

Percents

solving a variety of word problems that involve percents

 Math Skills

① $20 \times 50\%$

$= 20 \times$ ▢

$=$ ▢

② $60 \times 10\%$

$=$

$=$

③ $28 \times 7\%$

$=$

$=$

④ $250 \times 18\%$

$=$

$=$

⑤ $32 \times 16.5\%$

$=$

$=$

⑥ $8 \times 0.2\%$

$=$

$=$

⑦ **15% of 200**

$15 \div 100 = 0.15$

$0.15 \times 200 =$

$\boxed{30}$

⑧ **8% of 32**

⑨ **34% of 0.85**

$34 \div 100 = 0.34\%$

$0.34 \times 0.85 =$

$\boxed{0.289}$

⑩ **125% of 4**

⑪ **14.25% of 400**

⑫ **8.15% of 32**

⑬ Find the percent change

a. from 10 to 6.

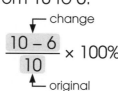
$\dfrac{10 - 6}{10} \times 100\%$

change
original

$=$ _____

$=$ _____

b. from 80 to 110.

c. from 21.36 to 24.03.

d. from 16.75 to 10.72.

ISBN: 978-1-77149-206-5

Problem Solving

Try This!

Eliza puts $500 into a savings account at a simple interest rate of 2% annually. How much interest will she earn after 6 years?

Solution:

Step 1: **Find the interest earned.**

$$\text{Interest} = \text{Principal} \times \frac{\text{Interest Rate}}{} \times \frac{\text{Time}}{\text{(in years)}}$$

$$= \$500 \times 2\% \times 6$$

$$= \$\boxed{}$$

> A principal is an initial money amount that can earn interest. In this question, $500 is the principal.

Step 2: **Write a concluding sentence.**

Eliza will earn $\boxed{}$ after 6 years.

① Rodney invests $1300 at an annual simple interest rate of 5%.

a. How much interest will he earn in 3 years?

$$1300 \times 5\% \times 3 = 195$$

Rodney will earn $\underline{195}$ in 3 years.

b. How much interest will he earn in 3 months?

$$195 \div 3 = 65$$
$$65 \div 4 = 16.25$$

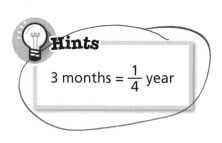

Hints

3 months = $\frac{1}{4}$ year

Rodney will earn $\underline{16.25}$ in 3 months.

ISBN: 978-1-77149-206-5

② Howard puts $2200 into a savings account at a 4.5% interest rate.

a. How much interest will he earn after 9 months?

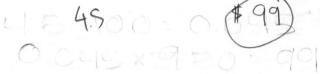

45    $99

0.045 × 9 = 99

Howard will earn $ 74.25 after 9 months.

b. How much will he have in the account after 6 years?

Howard will have $_____ after 6 years.

③ Mr. Willy borrows $3500 at an annual simple interest rate of 3.6%.

a. How much interest will he have to pay after $2\frac{1}{2}$ years?

Mr. Willy will have to pay $_____ in interest.

b. How much will he have to pay in total after 5 years?

Mr. Willy will have to pay $_____ in total.

ISBN: 978-1-77149-206-5

④ A local credit union offers an investment plan with a 2% simple interest every half a year. How much interest will an investment of $1500 make after 3 years?

Hints

Find out how many half-years there are in 3 years. Use that as the time.

The investment will make $_____ in interest.

⑤ Martha has earned a total of $96 in interest after investing $1200 four years ago. What was her annual simple interest rate?

Martha's annual simple interest rate was _____ .

⑥ Roberta invested $695 at an annual simple interest rate of 5%. After how many years will she have a total of $834?

Roberta will have a total of $834 after _____ years.

⑦ Danny has $350 to invest. How long will it take him to double the investment if the annual simple interest rate is 12.5%?

It will take Danny _____ years.

⑧ A clothing store created an advertisement to promote their clothes. Round all money amounts to 2 decimal places.

Hat
$25.75

Sweater
$68

Jacket
$135

Pants
$42.99

Shoes
$89.50

AUTUMN
by NEW MATERIAL

a. How much will the jacket cost if there is a 14% sales tax?

_____

b. How much more will the sweater cost than the pants after tax?

_____

c. As part of their promotion, the store is giving a 15% discount before tax for all items. How much money will be saved on the shoes after tax?

_____

d. Is $345 enough to purchase the entire outfit with the discount and tax?

_____

ISBN: 978-1-77149-206-5

⑨ Best Electronics bought 20 televisions from a wholesaler at the cost of $1080 each and will sell them at a profit margin of 30%.

   a. How much profit will Best Electronics make from selling the 20 televisions?

      _____

   b. John, a salesperson, earns a 3.5% commission on the sales price of each television. How much commission will he earn if he sells 5 televisions?

      _____

⑩ The regular price of a dress is $200 and it is currently on sale at 20% off. Marsha's membership card offers an additional 15% off the discounted price. How much will Marsha pay for the dress after a 13% tax?

_____

⑪
> When Ontario merged its GST and PST into the HST, gasoline became taxed at 13% instead of 5%.

What is the difference of $45.50 worth of gasoline before and after the merge?

_____

⑫ The price of a couch is marked down by 75%. If the final cost of the couch is $1590.40 after a sales tax of 12%, what was its original price?

⑬ A cellphone was $290 and is now $216.05. What is the discount rate?

⑭ It was 15°C in the morning. The temperature then rose to 16.5°C by noon. What was the temperature change in percent?

⑮ The minimum wage in Alberta was raised from $11.20 to $12.60 in 2016. What was the raise in percent?

⑯ Baby Theo weighed 7.54 kg last month. He weighs 8.294 kg this month. How much weight has he gained in percent?

ISBN: 978-1-77149-206-5

⑰ Shane has $3000 to invest. He invests $1250 at an 8% annual simple interest rate for 3 years and the rest at 5% for 2 years. How much interest will he earn in total?

_____

⑱ In 2016, Carla's income was $60 000. She paid the federal tax of 15% on the first $45 282 and 20.5% on the remaining amount. How much federal tax did she pay?

_____

⑲ Ms. Li earns 1.5% of the price of each product she sells as a commission. She earned a commission of $24.54 on a fridge.

a. What was the price of the fridge?

_____

b. The cost of the fridge was $1766.88 after tax. What was the tax rate?

_____

c. If the fridge is sold at 15% off, what will Ms. Li's commission be? What will the cost of the fridge be after tax?

_____

Ratios, Proportions, and Rates

solving a variety of word problems that involve ratios, proportions, and rates

Math Skills

Ratio

① dots to stripes = _____ : _____

② stripes to all = _____

③ small to big = _____

④ small with dots to big with stripes = _____

⑤ all to small with stripes = _____

⑥ big with dots to all = _____

Proportion

⑦ Complete the tables.

a. The cost of meat is proportional to its weight.

Weight (kg)	Cost
2	$10.56
4	
	$42.24

b. The distance travelled is proportional to the amount of time travelled.

Time (h)	Distance (km)
3	195
4	
	390

Rate

⑧ 6 oranges for $4.74

$_____ /orange

⑨ 2.4 L in 5 days

_____ L/day

⑩ 8 eggs for 24 muffins

_____ muffins/egg

⑪ 336 words in 8 min

_____ words/min

⑫ 3 books for $36.75

$_____ /book

⑬ 22.5 m in 15 s

_____ m/s

ISBN: 978-1-77149-206-5

Problem Solving

A 2-m long string weighs 5 g. What is the weight of a 7-m long string?

Solution:

Step 1: **Set up a proportion.**

 The length of a string is directly proportional to its weight.

$$\frac{2}{5} = \frac{7}{w}$$ ← length
← weight

Step 2: **Cross multiply to solve.**

$$\frac{2}{5} \times \frac{7}{w}$$

$$2w = 5 \times 7$$

$$w = \boxed{}$$

> It does not matter which quantity is the numerator or denominator as long as they are the same for both ratios in the proportion.

Step 3: **Write a concluding sentence.**

The weight of a 7-m long string

is $\boxed{}$ g.

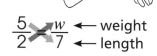

$$\frac{5}{2} \times \frac{w}{7}$$ ← weight
← length

$$2w = 5 \times 7$$

$$w = ?$$

① Refer to the question above. What is the weight of

a. a 9-m long string?

b. a 1.5-m string?

The weight is _____ g.

The weight is _____ g.

② Collette is using her grandma's recipe to make crepes. She wants to make 6 servings.

Grandma's Crepes
(for 4 servings)

300 g of flour
100 mL of water
250 mL of milk
40 g of butter
2 eggs

a. How much of each ingredient does she need?

- flour

Collette needs _____ g of flour.

- water

- milk

Collette needs _____ mL of water.

Collette needs _____ mL of milk.

- butter

- egg

Collette needs _____ g of butter.

Collette needs _____ egg(s).

b.

I top every 2 servings with 65 g of berries.

How much berries does she need?

Collette

Collette needs _____ g of berries.

ISBN: 978-1-77149-206-5

③ I enlarged a photo at a printing shop. The original photo measures 10 cm by 15 cm.

a. If the length of the enlarged photo is 37.5 cm, what is its width?

The width of the enlarged photo is _____ cm.

b. If the width of the enlarged photo is 15 cm, what is its length?

The length of the enlarged photo is _____ cm.

④ If the exchange rate is CAD $1.30 to USD $1, how much

a. is USD $20 worth in CAD?

CAD = Canadian Dollar
USD = United States Dollar

It is worth CAD $_____ .

b. is CAD $13 worth in USD?

c. is CAD $11.05 worth in USD?

It is worth USD $_____ .

It is worth USD $_____ .

⑤ 2 kg of fertilizer is needed for 8 kg of grass seeds.

　a. What is the ratio of fertilizer to grass seeds?

_____

　b. How much fertilizer is needed for 10 kg of grass seeds?

_____

⑥ At a bake sale, the ratio of the number of chocolate chip cookies to the number of all cookies sold was 7:11. If 55 cookies were sold, how many of them were chocolate chip cookies?

_____

⑦ A café has a rewards program in which there is 1 free drink for every 8 drinks purchased. How many drinks does Agatha need to purchase to get 10 free drinks?

_____

⑧ The amount of time Joey spends on jogging to swimming is 2:3. If she spends 35 min on jogging each day, how much time does she spend on swimming?

_____

ISBN: 978-1-77149-206-5

⑨ Winnie's soccer team has a win to loss ratio of 9:7.

a. If the team won 27 games, how many games did they lose?

_____

b. If the team lost 14 games, how many games did they win?

_____

⑩

> For two shapes to be similar, the ratios of their corresponding sides must be the same. Determine whether or not each triangle described below is similar to this one.

a. Right Triangle A has a base of 4.5 cm and a height of 6 cm.

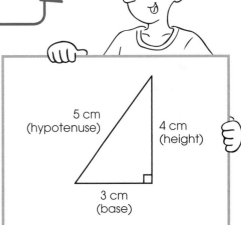

5 cm
(hypotenuse)

4 cm
(height)

3 cm
(base)

_____

b. Right Triangle B has a base of 6 cm and a hypotenuse of 8 cm.

_____

ISBN: 978-1-77149-206-5

⑪ Marc has driven 226.5 km in 3 hours.

a. What is his speed?

Marc

_____

b. How far will Marc travel in total if he continues at this speed for 5 hours?

_____

⑫ Apple Mart sells 6 apples for $3.54 and Fresh Market sells 8 apples for $4.32. Which store has the better deal?

_____

⑬ At a bulk food store, 100 g of dried kiwis cost $4.15.

a. How much dried kiwis can $10.79 buy?

_____

b. How much do 340 g of dried kiwis cost?

_____

ISBN: 978-1-77149-206-5

⑭ A projector shows an image that measures 1.6 m by 2.4 m. If one side of the original image is 12 cm, what are the possible lengths of the other side?

_____

⑮ Joe's new car can travel 150 km with 12 L of gas, while his old car had a fuel economy of 14.8 km/L. How much more fuel efficient is Joe's new car?

_____

⑯ Camilla wants to make an organic cleaning solution using vinegar, baking soda, and water. There is 30 mL of vinegar for every 5 g of baking soda, and the ratio of water to vinegar is 16:4.

a. If Camilla uses 40 g of baking soda, how much water should she add?

_____

b. What is the ratio of baking soda to water?

_____

c. How much baking soda is needed for a 620-mL solution?

_____

ISBN: 978-1-77149-206-5

Pythagorean Relationship

solving a variety of word problems that involve Pythagorean relationship

 Math Skills

① Colour the triangles that can be applied with the Pythagorean theorem. Then highlight their hypotenuses in red.

Pythagorean Theorem

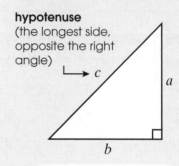

hypotenuse (the longest side, opposite the right angle)

$$a^2 + b^2 = c^2$$

The square of the hypotenuse is equal to the sum of the squares of a and b in a right triangle.

② Find the missing side of each triangle.

a.

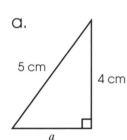

5 cm

4 cm

a

$a^2 + 4^2 = 5^2$

$a^2 + \boxed{} = \boxed{}$

$a^2 = \boxed{}$

$\sqrt{a^2} = \sqrt{\boxed{}}$

$a = \boxed{}$

b.

2.5 m

d

6 m

c.

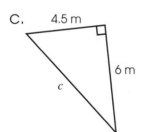

4.5 m

6 m

c

d.

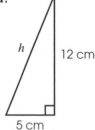

h

12 cm

5 cm

40

ISBN: 978-1-77149-206-5

Problem Solving

Try This!

A 3-m long ladder is leaning against a wall. The bottom of the ladder is 2 m away from the wall. How high up does the ladder reach on the wall?

Solution:

Step 1: Make a simple diagram to illustrate the scenario.

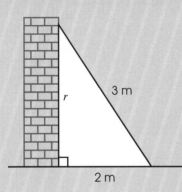

3 m

r

2 m

Step 2: Use the Pythagorean theorem to solve r.

$$r^2 + 2^2 = 3^2$$

$$r^2 + \boxed{} = \boxed{}$$

$$r^2 = \boxed{}$$

$$\sqrt{r^2} = \sqrt{\boxed{}}$$

$$r = \boxed{}$$

Step 3: Write a concluding sentence.

The ladder reaches $\boxed{}$ m on the wall.

① Refer to the question above.

a. If the ladder is 1 m away from the wall, how high up does it reach?

b. If the ladder is extended to 4 m and is 2 m away from the wall, how high up does it reach?

It reaches _____ m.

It reaches _____ m.

② A flagpole is tethered to the ground with a wire as shown. How long is the wire?

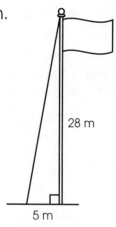

28 m

5 m

The wire is _____ m long.

③ A right triangle has a base of 12 cm. Its height is 23 cm longer than the base. What is its hypotenuse?

Its hypotenuse is _____ cm.

④ A right triangle has a base of 16.3 cm and a hypotenuse of 24.6 cm. What is its height?

Its height is _____ cm.

⑤ A right isosceles triangle has a hypotenuse of 26 cm. What are the lengths of its other sides?

Tips

An isosceles triangle has 2 sides of equal length.

The lengths of its other sides are _____ cm and _____ cm.

ISBN: 978-1-77149-206-5

⑥ The perimeter of an equilateral triangle is 60 cm. What is its area?

Hints

An equilateral triangle is made up of 2 right triangles.

Its area is _____ cm².

⑦ Two telephone poles are 19 m and 22 m tall. They are 30 m apart. If a wire connects the tops of the poles, what is the length of the wire?

Hints

Find the difference between the heights of the poles first.

The length of the wire is _____ m.

⑧ Ed's location is shown. Is he closer to the fire hydrant or the mailbox?

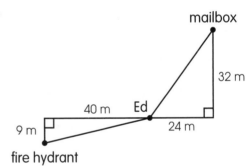

Ed is closer to the _____ .

⑨
> I drew a triangle with sides of 16 cm, 21 cm, and 26 cm. Is it a right triangle? Explain.

It _____ a right triangle because _____
   is/is not

_____ .

ISBN: 978-1-77149-206-5

⑩ Vera and Simon started at the same location. Vera has walked 35 m west and Simon has walked 12 m north. How far apart are they?

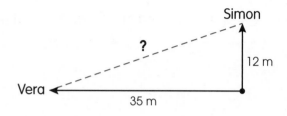

⑪ Two ferries are leaving from the same port. How far apart will they be if one ferry travels 2.5 km south and the other travels 4 km west?

⑫ Regina's boat left the port and sailed 13 km west and 5 km north.

a. How far away was Regina's boat from the port?

b. The boat then sailed another 6 km north. How much farther from the port is the boat now than before?

ISBN: 978-1-77149-206-5

⑬ Luke has a rectangular farm that measures 8 m by 20 m. He wants to add a fence that runs diagonally. What will the length of the fence be?

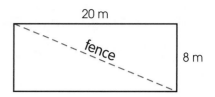

⑭ Ryan puts posts down at the 3 points shown. He wants to fence the triangular area. What length of fencing does he need?

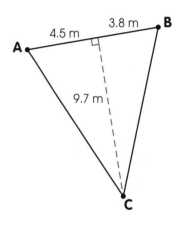

⑮ The diagonal of a square is 19.8 cm. What is the side length of the square?

⑯ The dimensions of a triangular frame are shown. What is the perimeter of the frame?

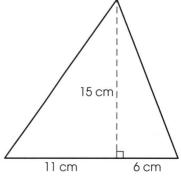

ISBN: 978-1-77149-206-5

⑰ The dimensions of Sylvia's house are shown.

   a. How tall is the house?

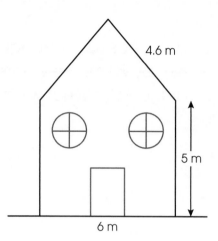

   _____

   b. What is the area of the front of the house?

   _____

⑱ Kyle is making a kite with the dimensions shown. He wants to add trimming around it. How much trimming does he need?

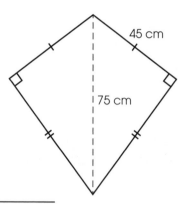

   _____

⑲ The trapezoid is divided into 2 right triangles.

   a. What are the lengths of x and y?

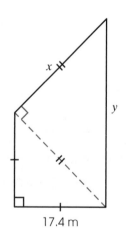

   _____

   b. What is the area of the trapezoid?

   _____

ISBN: 978-1-77149-206-5

⑳ Sandy designed a model of a bridge that hangs from a tower by a chain that is 27 cm long.

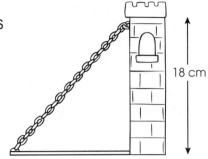

a. How long is the bridge?

_____

b. If Sandy lowers the anchor of the chain that is on the tower by 3 cm, how much shorter is the chain?

_____

㉑ Oliver places a square within a square as shown.

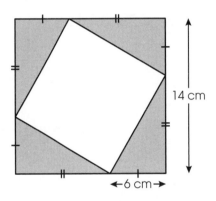

a. What is the side length of the smaller square?

_____

b. If Oliver cuts the smaller square into 4 identical right isosceles triangles, what will the perimeter of each triangle be?

_____

㉒ This trapezoid has an area of 96.72 cm². What is its perimeter?

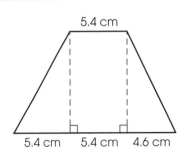

_____

ISBN: 978-1-77149-206-5

Circles

solving a variety of word problems that involve properties of circles, such as radius, diameter, circumference, and area

 Math Skills

①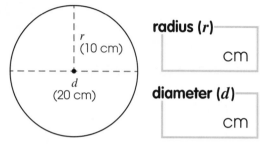

r (10 cm)

d (20 cm)

radius (r)

☐ cm

diameter (d)

☐ cm

Circumference (C) = $2\pi r$ or πd

$2\pi r$

= 2 × 3.14 × ☐

= ☐ (cm)

Area (A) = πr^2

πr^2

= 3.14 × ☐²

= ☐ (cm²)

②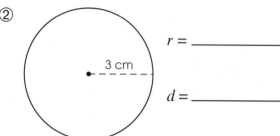

3 cm

$r =$ _____

$d =$ _____

C =

A =

③
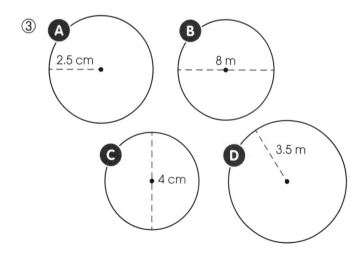

A 2.5 cm

B 8 m

C 4 cm

D 3.5 m

	Circumference	Area
A	_____ cm	_____ cm²
B	_____	_____
C	_____	_____
D	_____	_____

ISBN: 978-1-77149-206-5

 **Problem Solving**

Dominic ordered a medium pizza. It has a diameter of 30 cm. What is its area?

Solution:

Step 1: Find the radius.

$$r = \frac{d}{2}$$

$$= \frac{\boxed{}}{2}$$

$$= \boxed{}$$

A diameter is the length of a line that joins two points of a circle through the centre. A radius is the distance from the centre to a point of a circle. So, the radius is half of the diameter.

Step 2: Find the area.

$$A = \pi r^2$$

$$= \boxed{} \times \boxed{}^2$$

$$= \boxed{}$$

Step 3: Write a concluding sentence.

The area of the medium pizza is $\boxed{}$ cm².

① Refer to the question above. A large pizza has a diameter that is 5 cm longer.

a. What is the circumference of the large pizza?

The circumference is _____ cm.

b. What is its area?

Its area is _____ cm².

ISBN: 978-1-77149-206-5

② My hula hoop has a diameter of 1.3 m.

Karen

a. What is its circumference?

 Its circumference is ＿＿＿＿＿ m.

b. Karen has another hula hoop that has a radius of 0.55 m. What is its circumference?

 Its circumference is ＿＿＿＿＿ m.

③ The base of a carousel has a radius of 3.5 m. What is its circumference?

 Its circumference is ＿＿＿＿＿ m.

④ A circular fountain has a circumference of 3.5 m. What is the radius of the fountain?

 The radius of the fountain is ＿＿＿＿＿ m.

ISBN: 978-1-77149-206-5

⑤ Maverick made two circular coasters. The small coaster has a radius of 4 cm and the big one has a diameter of 12 cm.

a. What is the area of the small coaster?

The area of the small coaster is _____ cm².

b. What is the area of the big coaster?

The area of the big coaster is _____ cm².

c. Maverick wants to trim the edges of the coasters with a rope. How much rope does he need?

Maverick needs _____ cm of rope.

⑥ Terry baked a pita with a circumference of 16 cm. His sister baked a pita that has a radius of 5 cm. Whose pita is bigger? By how much?

_____'s pita is bigger by _____ cm².

ISBN: 978-1-77149-206-5

⑦ A round mirror has an area of 0.1 m². What is the diameter of the mirror in centimetres?

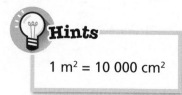

Hints

1 m² = 10 000 cm²

⑧ A Canadian toonie is made up of an inner circle with an outer ring. What is the area of the outer ring?

28 mm

17 mm

⑨ A tile design has a circle inside a square. What is the total area of the shaded parts?

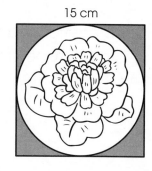

15 cm

⑩ Josephine measured her finger for a ring. She wrapped tape measure around her finger and measured 57 mm. What would the size of her ring be?

Ring Size	Diameter (mm)
7	17.3
8	18.2
9	19.0
10	19.8

ISBN: 978-1-77149-206-5

⑪ A toy car track consists of 2 quarter circles. How long is the track?

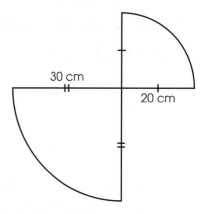

_____

⑫ Sebastian printed a label for his CD. What is the area of the label?

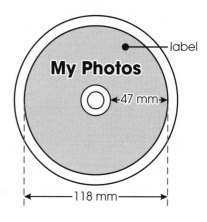

_____

⑬ A new skating rink is built as shown.

a. What is the area of the skating rink?

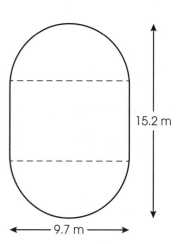

_____

b. What is the perimeter of the skating rink?

_____

ISBN: 978-1-77149-206-5

⑭ A bike tire has a radius of 17.5 cm. A car tire has a diameter of 45 cm.

a. How far does the bike travel in metres if its tire makes 100 rotations?

Hints

Find the circumference first.

_____

b. If the car travels a total of 141.3 m, how many times does its tire rotate?

_____

⑮ Eliza wants to draw a large circle that has an area that equals the sum of the areas of two smaller circles with diameters of 8 cm and 11 cm. What is the radius of the large circle?

_____

⑯ Grayson has a string that is π m long. He uses the string to form a circle.

a. What is the area of the circle?

_____

b. If Grayson doubled the length of the string, how much greater will the area of the circle be?

_____

ISBN: 978-1-77149-206-5

⑰ The difference between the circumferences of the 2 circles is 9.42 cm. What is the area of the shaded part?

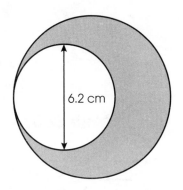

6.2 cm

_____

⑱ Jordan wants to draw a rectangle that has an area of 60.5 cm². What will the area of the largest possible semicircle that fits inside the rectangle be?

Hints

A semicircle is half of a circle. Make a sketch of the largest semicircle possible within a rectangle.

_____

⑲ A triangle is drawn inside a circle as shown. If the radius of the circle is 5 cm, what is the area of the circle not covered by the triangle?

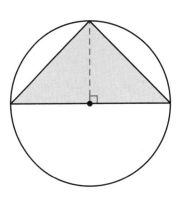

_____

⑳ A square tile as shown has an area of 96.04 cm².

  a. What is the perimeter of the star shape in the tile?

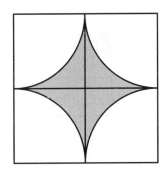

_____

  b. What is the area of the star shape in the tile?

_____

Volume and Surface Area

solving a variety of word problems that involve the volume and surface area of prisms, pyramids, cylinders, and spheres

 Math Skills

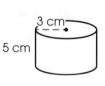 Volume:
$\pi r^2 h$

Surface Area:
$2\pi r^2 + 2\pi rh$

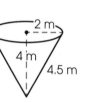 Volume:
$\frac{4}{3}\pi r^3$

Surface Area:
$4\pi r^2$

 Volume:
$\frac{1}{3}\pi r^2 h$

Surface Area:
$\pi rs + \pi r^2$

①

3 cm
5 cm

V:

S.A.:

②

1 cm

V:

S.A.:

③

2 m
4 m
4.5 m

V:

S.A.:

④

6 m
20 m

V:

S.A.:

⑤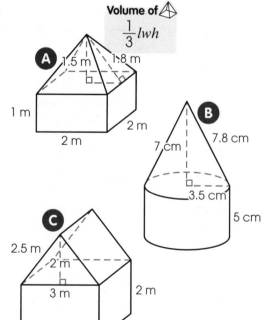

Volume of
$\frac{1}{3} lwh$

A
1.5 m   1.8 m
1 m
2 m
2 m

B
7 cm   7.8 cm
3.5 cm
5 cm

C
2.5 m
2 m
3 m
2 m
3 m

A

V: _____   S.A.: _____

B

V: _____   S.A.: _____

C

V: _____   S.A.: _____

ISBN: 978-1-77149-206-5

Problem Solving

Daven has a soup can that is a cylinder. It has a radius of 4 cm and a height of 12 cm. What is the volume of the soup can?

Solution:

Step 1: **Make a sketch of the cylinder.**

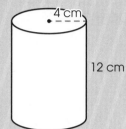

4 cm

12 cm

> A cylinder is simply a prism with circular faces. Therefore, to find its volume, multiply the area of its base with its height.

Step 2: **Find the volume.**

area of base ⌐ ⌐ height

$$V = \boxed{\pi r^2}\ \boxed{h}$$

$$= 3.14 \times \boxed{}^2 \times \boxed{}$$

$$= \boxed{}$$

Step 3: **Write a concluding sentence.**

The volume of the soup can is $\boxed{}$ cm³.

① A container for chips has a diameter of 7.8 cm and a height of 23 cm. What is its volume?

Chips

The volume of the container is _____ cm³.

ISBN: 978-1-77149-206-5

② Cyrus has a rod that is 1 m long and has a diameter of 2 cm.

a. What is its volume?

The volume of the rod is _____ cm³.

b. Cyrus wants to paint the rod. What is its surface area?

The surface area of the rod is _____ cm².

③ Linda made a 2-tiered cake as shown.

a. What is the volume of the cake?

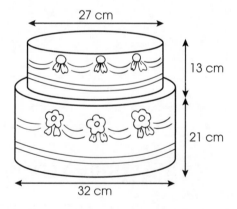

27 cm

13 cm

21 cm

32 cm

The volume of the cake is _____ cm³.

b. Linda needs to put icing on the top tier of the cake except its bottom. What is the area of the cake that needs icing?

The area of the cake that needs icing is _____ cm².

ISBN: 978-1-77149-206-5

④ Sophie made her own paper cup that has the dimensions shown.

a. What is the capacity of the paper cup?

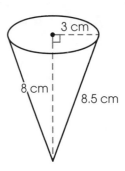

The capacity of the paper cup is _____ mL.

b. How much paper did Sophie use in cm²?

Sophie used _____ cm² of paper.

⑤

This ice cream cone has a height of 10 cm. The diameter of its base is 6 cm.

a. What is the capacity of the cone?

The capacity of the cone is _____ mL.

b. The outside of the cone will be coated with chocolate. What is the surface area that needs coating?

Hints

Use the Pythagorean theorem to find the missing measurement.

The surface area is _____ cm².

⑥ The diameter of a basketball is 24.26 cm.

   a. What is the volume of the basketball?

   _____

   b. What is the surface area of the basketball?

   _____

⑦ A green marble has a radius of 0.5 cm. A red marble has a radius that is twice the green marble's. What is the surface area of the red marble?

   _____

⑧ Don has an orange with a radius of 4 cm. If he cuts away $\frac{1}{4}$ of it, what will the volume and the surface area of the orange be?

   _____

ISBN: 978-1-77149-206-5

⑨ Riley has bought a 50-cm³ block of chocolate that is in the shape of a rectangular pyramid. If the area of the base is 16 cm², what is the height of the block of chocolate?

_____

⑩ Mina created a model of a pyramid for her history class project.

a. What is the volume of the pyramid?

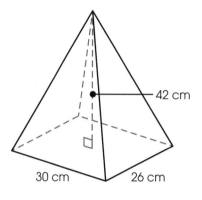

42 cm

30 cm   26 cm

_____

b. What is the surface area of the pyramid?

_____

⑪ Samantha made a triangular pyramid that is a Platonic solid. What is the surface area of the pyramid?

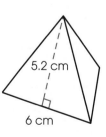

5.2 cm

6 cm

Tips

The faces of a Platonic solid are identical regular polygons.

_____

ISBN: 978-1-77149-206-5

⑫ Tania wants to cut a wooden block into a "T".

a. What will the volume of the "T" block be?

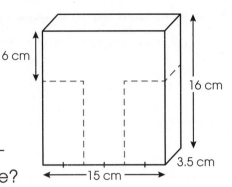

_____

b. What will the surface area of the "T" block be?

_____

⑬ Amy and Ruby are building their own dollhouses. Amy's dollhouse is made up of a triangular prism and a rectangular prism as shown.

a. What is the volume of Amy's dollhouse?

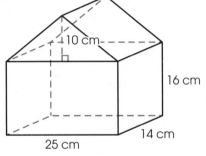

_____

b. Ruby's dollhouse has the same rectangular prism as Amy's, but the roof is a rectangular prism that has a height of 10 cm instead. What is the volume of Ruby's dollhouse?

_____

⑭ Kyle made a cup holder by cutting a cylinder out of a wooden block. What is the volume of the cup holder?

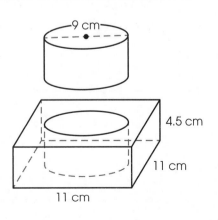

_____

ISBN: 978-1-77149-206-5

⑮ A cake is in the shape of half of a cylinder.

a. What is the volume of the cake?

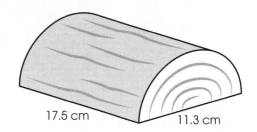

17.5 cm   11.3 cm

_____

b. Icing is added to the cake except its bottom. What will the total area covered with icing be?

_____

⑯ A machine has cut a cylinder into a solid that resembles 2 identical cones as shown.

a. By how much has the volume reduced?

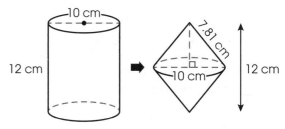

10 cm

12 cm   7.81 cm   12 cm   10 cm

_____

b. Has the surface area increased or decreased? By how much?

_____

⑰ A washer is a small hardware component. What is the volume of the washer?

Top view   **Side view**

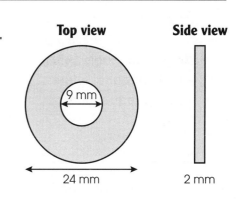

9 mm

24 mm   2 mm

_____

ISBN: 978-1-77149-206-5

Angles and Triangles

solving a variety of word problems that involve angles and properties of triangles

 Math Skills

①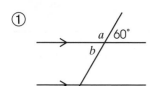

a = _____

b = _____

c = _____

②

x = _____

y = _____

z = _____

③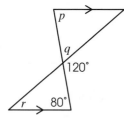

p = _____

q = _____

r = _____

④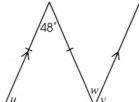

u = _____

v = _____

w = _____

Properties of Congruent Triangles

- **Side-side-side (SSS)**
  3 pairs of equal sides

- **Side-angle-side (SAS)**
  2 pairs of equal sides
  1 pair of equal angles

- **Angle-side-angle (ASA)**
  2 pairs of equal angles
  1 pair of equal sides

⑤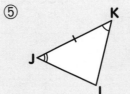

$\overline{JK}$ = _____

∠JKL = _____

∠KJL = _____

△JKL ≅ △_____ (__ S __)
└── congruent to

⑥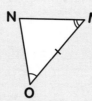

$\overline{AB}$ = _____

$\overline{AC}$ = _____

$\overline{BC}$ = _____

△ABC ≅ _____ (_____)

⑦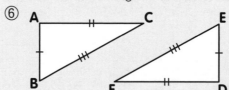

$\overline{XZ}$ = _____

∠XZY = _____

$\overline{YZ}$ = _____

△XYZ ≅ _____ (_____)

ISBN: 978-1-77149-206-5

Problem Solving

Try This!

Adrian drew a parallelogram. One of its angles measures 45°. What are the sizes of the other angles?

Consecutive interior angles are the angles that are on one side of a transversal and inside the two parallel lines. Their sum is 180°.

Solution:

Step 1: **Make a sketch of the parallelogram.**

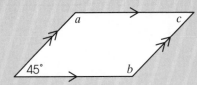

Consecutive Interior Angles

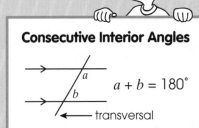

$a + b = 180°$

transversal

Step 2: **Find the angles.**

By consecutive interior angles:

$a + 45° = 180°$ $b + 45° = 180°$ $a + c = 180°$

$a = \boxed{}$ $b = \boxed{}$ $c = \boxed{}$

Step 3: **Write a concluding sentence.**

The sizes of the other angles are $\boxed{}$, $\boxed{}$, and $\boxed{}$.

① The diagram shows the intersection of 3 streets.

a. What is the size of the other angle that Bay Avenue and Oak Lane make?

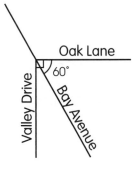

The size of the angle is _____ .

b. What are the sizes of the angles that Bay Avenue and Valley Drive make?

The sizes of the angles are _____ and _____ .

ISBN: 978-1-77149-206-5

② Loretta draws 2 diagonals of a rectangle that divide the rectangle into 4 isosceles triangles as shown. Find the angles.

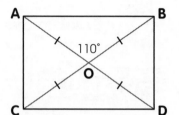

a. ∠COD

b. ∠AOC

∠COD is _____ .

∠AOC is _____ .

c. ∠ABO

d. ∠OAC

∠ABO is _____ .

∠OAC is _____ .

③ Gavin puts 5 congruent triangles together to form a regular pentagon.

a. What is a?

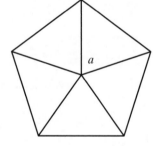

a is _____ .

b. What are the sizes of the angles in each triangle?

The sizes of the angles are _____ , _____ , and _____ .

ISBN: 978-1-77149-206-5

④ There are two pairs of parallel bike lanes as shown in a park.

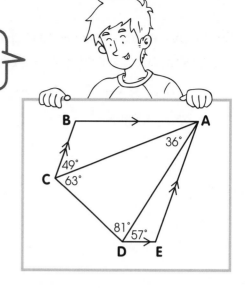

a. What is the measure of ∠BAD?

The measure of ∠BAD is _____ .

b. Are the measures of ∠CBA and ∠DEA equal? What are their measures?

_____ , the measures _____ equal. They are _____ and
  Yes/No   are/are not

_____ .

⑤ A pyramid has 2 levels.

a. Are the levels parallel?

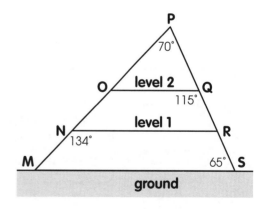

_____

b. Which level is parallel to the ground?

_____

ISBN: 978-1-77149-206-5

⑥ Draw each angle using a protractor. Then bisect each angle using a compass. What is the size of each bisected angle?

a. two 5-cm arms making a 60° angle

b. two 3.5-cm arms making a 130° angle

_____ _____

⑦ Draw each perpendicular bisector using a compass. What is the size of the angle that the bisector and the original line make?

a. bisecting a 6-cm line

b. bisecting a 5.4-cm line

_____ _____

⑧
Draw a perpendicular bisector on a 7-cm line. Then bisect one of its right angles twice. What is the size of the smallest bisected angle?

_____

ISBN: 978-1-77149-206-5

⑨ Help Hazel draw the 4 triangles described below.

a. a triangle with side lengths of 3 cm, 4 cm, and 2.5 cm

b. an isosceles triangle with two 70° angles with a side of 2.7 cm between them

c. a triangle with two 4-cm arms making a 40° angle

d. an equilateral triangle with side lengths of 4 cm

e. Hazel wants to draw a perpendicular bisector on one of the sides to divide the equilateral triangle into 2 equal triangles. What will the sizes of the angles of each identical triangle be?

f.
> Are there any congruent triangles? If so, what are their side lengths and angles?

⑩ Veronica arranges the congruent triangles to form a shape. What is the perimeter of the shape?

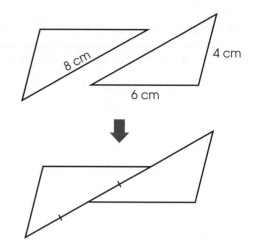

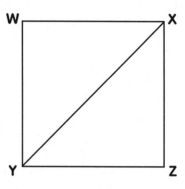

_____

⑪ Drawing the diagonal of a square creates 2 triangles. Show that the triangles are congruent

a. by SSS.

b. by SAS.

_____

c. by ASA.

_____   _____

⑫ The two ends of a 3.2-cm side in Marcus's triangle are two 30° angles. Nancy's triangle has two 2.1-cm arms that make a 120° angle. Draw both triangles. Are they congruent?

_____

ISBN: 978-1-77149-206-5

⑬ The map of hiking trails is shown.

a. Are △ABE and △DCE congruent?

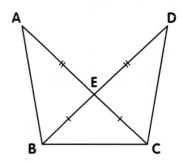

_____

b. Are $\overline{AB}$ and $\overline{DC}$ equal?

Triangles are congruent
by SSS (side-side-side),
SAS (side-angle-side), or
ASA (angle-side-angle).

_____

c. Are △ABC and △DCB congruent?

_____

⑭ Points X, Y, and Z are the midpoints of all the sides
of △ABC.

a. Are △AXY and △ZYX congruent?

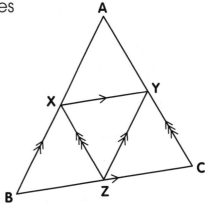

_____

b. Are △BXZ and △ZYC congruent?

_____

ISBN: 978-1-77149-206-5

Cartesian Coordinate Plane

solving a variety of word problems that involve finding the distance between coordinates and transformations

  Math Skills

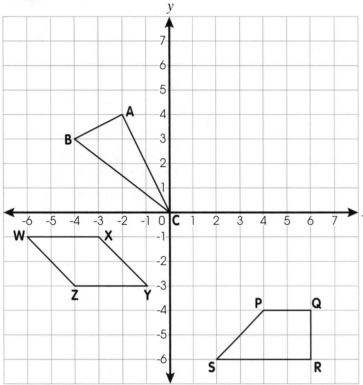

① Write the coordinates of each shape's vertices.

Shape ABC

A(_____)

B(_____)   C(_____)

Shape PQRS

P(_____)   Q(_____)

R(_____)   S(_____)

Shape WXYZ

W(_____)   X(_____)

Y(_____)   Z(_____)

② Perform the transformations of each shape. Then write the coordinates of the vertices of the transformed image.

a. Reflect Shape ABC in the x-axis. Then rotate it 90° counterclockwise about (0,0).

A'(   )   B'(   )   C'(   )

b. Reflect Shape PQRS in the x-axis. Then reflect it in the y-axis.

P'(   )   Q'(   )   R'(   )   S'(   )

c. Reflect Shape WXYZ in the y-axis. Then translate it 4 units up and 1 unit to the right.

W'(   )   X'(   )   Y'(   )   Z'(   )

③ Which transformed shape is in each quadrant?

a. Quadrant I :_____   b. Quadrant II :_____

c. Quadrant III :_____   d. Quadrant IV :_____

ISBN: 978-1-77149-206-5

Problem Solving

Hailey drew a triangle as shown. She reflected the triangle in the *y*-axis. Then she rotated it 180° about (0,0). What are the coordinates of the image's vertex that lies in Quadrant III?

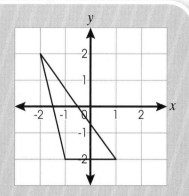

Solution:

Step 1: Do the reflection.

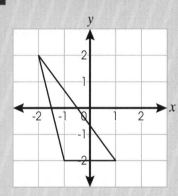

Step 2: Do the rotation.

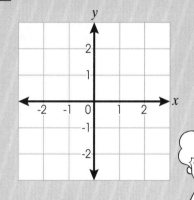

Step 3: Write a concluding sentence.

The coordinates of the vertex

are _____ .

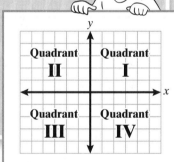

① Refer to the question above.

a. What are the coordinates of the vertex that lies in Quadrant II?

   The coordinates of the vertex are _____ .

b. What is the area of the image?

   The area of the image is _____ square units.

② Farmer Ken is making a layout for 3 enclosures for his vegetables.

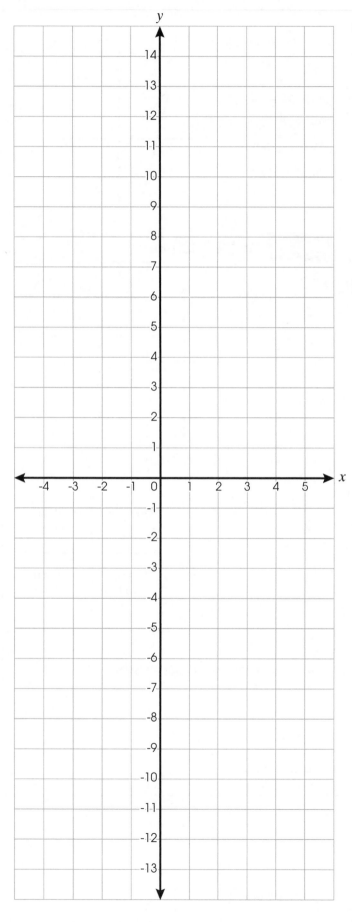

a. Plot the points and draw the enclosure for each type of vegetable.

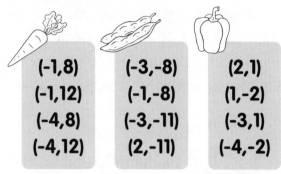

(-1,8)	(-3,-8)	(2,1)
(-1,12)	(-1,-8)	(1,-2)
(-4,8)	(-3,-11)	(-3,1)
(-4,12)	(2,-11)	(-4,-2)

b. Find the perimeter and area of each enclosure.

• carrots

The perimeter is _____ units and the area is _____ square units.

• peas

The perimeter is _____ units and the area is _____ square units.

• peppers

The perimeter is _____ units and the area is _____ square units.

ISBN: 978-1-77149-206-5

c. Perform the transformations for each enclosure of vegetables.

Rotate it 180° about (0,7). Then translate it 9 units down and 1 unit to the left.

Rotate it 90° counterclockwise about (-3,-8). Then reflect it in the *x*-axis.

Rotate it 270° clockwise about (2,1). Then translate it 6 units up and 1 unit to the left.

d. What are the coordinates of the vertices of each transformed enclosure?

- carrots: _____

- peas: _____

- peppers: _____

e.
> Fertilizer is added to the soil in Quadrant II. Which vegetable enclosure will have fertilizer before the transformations?

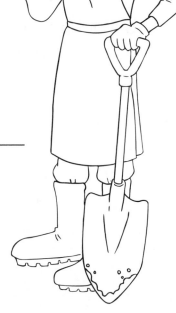

_____

f. Which vegetable enclosure is transformed to

- Quadrant I?

_____

- Quadrant IV?

_____

ISBN: 978-1-77149-206-5

③ Cynthia and her friends drew the shapes below.

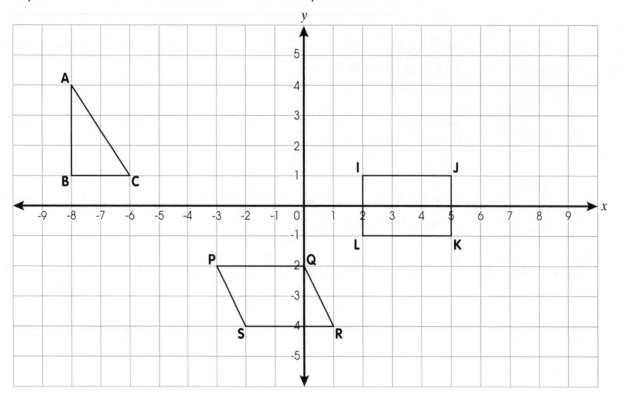

Read what each child did to each shape. Do the transformations on the grid. Then write the coordinates of the vertices of the images and describe the transformations.

a. Cynthia translated Point C of the triangle to (-4,2).

Coordinates

_____

_____

b. Karson rotated the rectangle so that Point L is at (-2,1).

Coordinates

_____

_____

c. Ryan reflected the parallelogram so that Point S is at (-2,4).

Coordinates

_____

_____

ISBN: 978-1-77149-206-5

d. What are the area and the perimeter of each image?

Hints

Use the Pythagorean theorem to find the hypotenuse.

- triangle

- rectangle

- parallelogram

e. Which shape and its image lie in the same quadrant? Which quadrant are they in?

f. Which image lies on the x-axis? Write the coordinates of the points that lie on the x-axis.

g. Which image lies on the y-axis? Write the coordinates of the points that lie on the y-axis.

ISBN: 978-1-77149-206-5

④ A portable classroom is shown on the grid. Write the coordinates of the vertices of the classroom if it is

a. translated 3 units to the left.

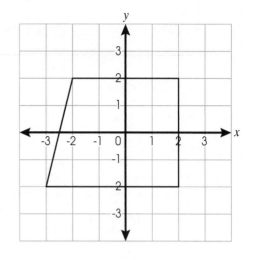

_____

b. translated 3 units to the right and 2 units up.

c. translated 2 units to the left and 3 units down.

_____   _____

⑤ New trees are planted so that they are a reflection of the old trees. The old trees are at (4,6), (3,-2), (-2,8), and (-1,0). What will the coordinates of the new trees be if they are

a. reflected in the x-axis?

Reflection in the x-axis
$(x,y) \rightarrow (x,-y)$

Reflection in the y-axis
$(x,y) \rightarrow (-x,y)$

_____

b. reflected in the y-axis?

_____

ISBN: 978-1-77149-206-5

⑥ Describe the transformation each child made.

a. Alan translated a point at (2,3) to (5,1).

_____

b. Eddie reflected a point at (1,-5) to (1,5).

_____

c. Josie rotated a point from (-1,-1) to (1,1).

_____

d. Ian translated a point from (1,2) to (-5,5). Then he rotated it to (5,5).

_____

e. If the transformed points are the vertices of a shape, what is the shape? What is the area of the shape?

_____

⑦ What is the distance between the point (-2,-4) and

a. its reflection in the y-axis?

_____

b. its 180° rotation about the origin?

Tips

The origin is (0,0).

_____

ISBN: 978-1-77149-206-5

Polynomials and Equations

solving a variety of word problems that involve polynomials and equations

 Math Skills

① Simplify.

a. $4x + 3x + 7$ _____

b. $6x - 3x + x$ _____

c. $6x(x^2)$ _____

d. $(-6xy^2)(2x^2y)$ _____

e. $(2m)^3n^0$ _____

f. $(2s^3) \div (8s^2)$ _____

g. $\dfrac{6ab^2}{2ab}$ _____

h. $\dfrac{-15x^3y^4}{5x^4y}$ _____

i. $\dfrac{(6m)(7n^{-2})}{(3m^{-6})(2n)}$ _____

j. $\dfrac{(-2)^2p^{-6}q^3}{(2pq)(4q^2)}$ _____

k. $(4x^2y - 10xy + 7xy^2) + (2xy - 7xy^2 + 6y^2)$ _____

l. $-(2ab + 4bc + 3ac) - (3ac + 6ab - 8bc)$ _____

② Solve.

a. $22 - 2c = 3c + 7$

b. $5(2t - 6) = 16$

c. $2(3k + 1) = -4(k + 3)$

d. $\dfrac{-2t - 1}{4t + 2} = 3$

e. $3m + 1 = \dfrac{6m - 2}{4}$

f. $\dfrac{2}{3}(4r - 1) = 3r + \dfrac{1}{3}$

g. $0.6t = 1.5(t + 1.2)$

h. $1.3(u - 11) = 15.8 - 2.2u$

i. $\dfrac{5}{(7 - u)} = \dfrac{3}{(u + 3)}$

ISBN: 978-1-77149-206-5

 **Problem Solving**

A rectangular field has a perimeter of 140 m. Its length is 2 units more than 3 times its width. What is the width of the field?

Solution:

Step 1: | **Illustrate the problem.**

$3w + 2$

w

Step 2: | **Set up and solve the equation.**

$(3w + 2 + w) \times 2 = 140$

$(4w + 2) \times 2 = 140$ ⟵ Simplify the L.H.S.

$\boxed{}\ w + \boxed{} = 140$

$\boxed{}\ w = \boxed{}$ ⟵ Isolate the term with w.

$w = \boxed{}$ ⟵ Solve for w.

Step 3: | **Write a concluding sentence.**

The width of the field is $\boxed{}$ m.

① The width of a table is half its length. The perimeter of the table is 6 m. What is its width?

The width of the table is _____ m.

② Doris has $20, which is $7 less than 3 times Barry's money. How much money does Barry have?

Barry has $_____ .

③ Renting a bike costs $6 plus $1.50 for each hour. If a family paid $30 in total for 4 bikes, for how long did they rent the bikes?

They rented the bikes for _____ h.

④ Mimi has cut out a wooden board that is in the shape of a trapezoid. If the perimeter of the board is 5.4 m, what is its height?

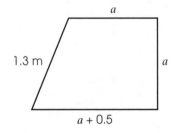

The height of the board is _____ m.

⑤ A swimming pool has a length that doubles its width. A rope divides the pool into a kids' section at one fourth of the length. If the kids' section is 8 m², what is the width of the pool?

The width of the pool is _____ m.

ISBN: 978-1-77149-206-5

⑥ Toby says, "In 5 years, I will be 4 years older than twice my age 3 years ago." How old is Toby now?

Toby is _____ years old now.

⑦ Ryan's jogging path is shown. After 5 laps, he will have run 13 km. What is the length of each side of the path?

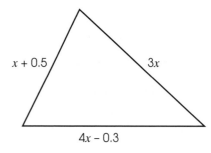

$x + 0.5$ $3x$

$4x - 0.3$

* not drawn to scale

The lengths of the sides are _____ km, _____ km, and _____ km.

⑧ Clara and Leo are having a race. Clara will give Leo a 17.5-m head start. Clara runs 8.5 m/s while Leo runs 6.75 m/s.

a. How long will it take Clara to catch up to Leo?

It will take Clara _____ s.

b. How long will it take Clara to run 28 m past Leo?

It will take Clara _____ s.

ISBN: 978-1-77149-206-5

⑨ Danielle has rearranged a square fence into a rectangular fence. The fence is measured in metres.

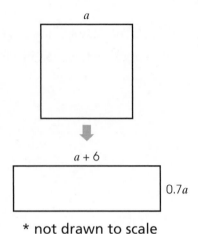

a. Danielle used all the old fencing. What is the perimeter of the new fence?

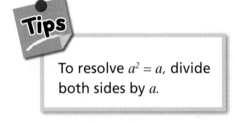

* not drawn to scale

_____

b. If the area remains the same, what was the area enclosed by the old fence?

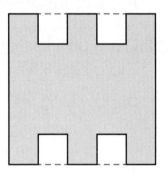

Tips

To resolve $a^2 = a$, divide both sides by a.

_____

⑩ 4 identical small squares are cut from a big square. The side length of each small square is $\frac{1}{5}$ of the big square.

a. If the area of the shaded part is 525 cm², what was the area of the big square?

_____

b. What is the perimeter of the shape?

_____

ISBN: 978-1-77149-206-5

⑪ Laura and Lindsay had an equal amount of money. Laura bought 6 doughnuts and 5 drinks with $2.05 left, and Lindsay bought 10 doughnuts and 3 drinks with $4.75 left.

a. If a doughnut cost $0.65, how much did a drink cost?

_____

b. How much money did Laura and Lindsay have altogether?

_____

⑫ Roger, Steve, and Tyler played a game of basketball. Steve scored 1 point less than twice Roger's score and Tyler scored 2 more points than 3 times Roger's score.

a. If Steve scored half as many points as Tyler, how many points did Roger score?

_____

b. Alternatively, if a total of 13 points were scored, how many points did each player score?

_____

ISBN: 978-1-77149-206-5

⑬ There is a rectangular walkway in a square garden that has a side length of 10 m. The length of the walkway triples its width.

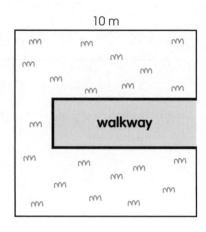

a. What is the width of the walkway if the area of the remaining garden is 81.25 m²?

_____

b. Fencing will be added on the 3 sides of the walkway as shown. How much is each metre of fencing if the total cost is $245?

_____

⑭ Anthony has $20.50. The number of toonies that he has is twice the number of loonies, and the number of quarters is half the number of loonies.

a. How many loonies does he have?

_____

b. How many coins does he have in all?

_____

c. How much more money does he have in toonies than in quarters?

_____

ISBN: 978-1-77149-206-5

⑮ A driveway is a square with a side length of 4.5 m. If the driveway is extended so that its perimeter is increased by 1.2 m, what is the area of the extended driveway?

_____

⑯ Tyson drove to the beach in 1.5 h at 60 km/h. How much faster would his return trip be if he drove 15 km/h faster?

_____

⑰

I weighed some fruits on a scale and recorded their weights below.

a. How many limes equal the weight of 1 orange?

2 apples	= 3 lemons
2 apples	= 5 limes
3 oranges	= 3 lemons + 4 limes

_____

b. If 4 apples are on one side of the scale and 3 oranges are on the other, how many limes are needed to balance the scale?

_____

c. An orange weighs 0.18 kg and a lemon weighs 0.1 kg. What is the weight of a lime?

_____

Inequalities

solving a variety of word problems that involve inequalities

Math Skills

① Circle the possible values of the unknown in each inequality.

a. $x > 2$

Possible values

-1   3   2   8

b. $x > -1$

Possible values

-7   0   -2   0.5

c. $x \geq 4$

Possible values

1   5   1.2   4.5

d. $x \leq -6$

Possible values

-1   -6   0   2

e. $-1 > x > 3$

Possible values

-2   1   3   -0.5

f. $0 \leq x < 8$

Possible values

3.8   6.3   0.7   -2.1

g. $-5 < x \leq 1$

Possible values

2   -5   -1   5

h. $-3 \geq x > -7$

Possible values

5   -7   -3   -4

i. $4 > x \geq -5$

Possible values

5   1   -4   0

② Solve the inequalities. Then check the set of numbers that match each unknown.

a. $2x > 4$

Ⓐ 5, 3.2, 2

Ⓑ 2.1, 3, 4

b. $2 - w < 3$

Ⓐ 0.25, 4, -0.8

Ⓑ 2, -1, 0

c. $3y + 2 \leq 11$

Ⓐ -1, -0.1, 3

Ⓑ 0.5, 4, -8

d. $3 \geq 2m + 1$

Ⓐ 0.7, 1.1, 2.6

Ⓑ 0.3, -6, -2.4

e. $-5v < 25$

Ⓐ 1.9, -5, 4

Ⓑ -4, -2, 0.7

f. $16 \geq -6z - 8$

Ⓐ -3, -6, 1.6

Ⓑ -2, -4, 0

ISBN: 978-1-77149-206-5

 **Problem Solving**

Ellen is thinking of a number. She says, "The product of my number and -2 is greater than 4." Find 2 possible numbers Ellen could be thinking of.

Solution:

Step 1: **Set up the inequality.**

$-2x > 4$

Step 2: **Solve the inequality.**

$-2x > 4$

$-2x \div \boxed{} < 4 \div \boxed{}$

$x < \boxed{}$

Solve an inequality as if you are solving an equation. However, when multiplying or dividing a negative number, make sure that the direction of the sign is reversed.

Step 3: **Write a concluding sentence.**

Ellen's number could be $\boxed{}$ or $\boxed{}$.

① A box has balls that are labelled with integers from -10 to 10. Janice and Adrian each picked a ball.

a. Janice says, "My number minus 3 is greater than 6." Which number did Janice pick?

Janice picked _____ .

b. Adrian says, "My number times 3 is less than -27." Which number did Adrian pick?

Adrian picked _____ .

ISBN: 978-1-77149-206-5

② Anita bought 2 sandwiches with a $6-off coupon. If the total cost was greater than $0, what was the cost of one sandwich?

The cost of one sandwich was _____ $_____ .
<u>greater than/less than</u>

③ A pizza shop advertises that it will complete deliveries in less than 30 minutes or the pizza is free. If it takes 12 minutes to make the pizza, how much time is left for the delivery before the pizza becomes free?

There are _____ _____ minutes left before the pizza
<u>more than/less than</u>
becomes free.

④ A test consists of 2 parts. The questions in Part 1 are worth 2 points each and the questions in Part 2 are worth 3 points each.

a. If Robin only answered 2 questions correctly in Part 2 but still passed the test, how many questions in Part 1 did he answer correctly?

Hints

A score of 50 or higher is a passing score.

Robin answered _____ _____ questions correctly in Part 1.
<u>at least/at most</u>

b. If Cass answered 21 questions in Part 1 correctly and she got over 90 points, how many questions in Part 2 were answered correctly?

Cass answered _____ _____ questions correctly in Part 2.
<u>more than/less than</u>

ISBN: 978-1-77149-206-5

⑤ Martha is planning a bake sale to raise at least $200. If she has 40 muffins, how much should she charge for each muffin?

Martha should charge _____ $_____ for each muffin.
<u>at least/at most</u>

⑥ A weighing scale has a maximum weight limit of 5 kg. Reza has placed 4 water bottles and a 3-kg juice carton on the scale, but the total weight exceeds the limit. At least how much does each water bottle weigh?

Each water bottle weighs _____ _____ kg.
<u>more than/less than</u>

⑦ Leon splits his 126 magnet collection evenly into a number of groups.

a. If each group has at least 18 magnets, how many groups does Leon have?

Leon has _____ _____ groups of magnets.
<u>at least/at most</u>

b. If there are at most 14 magnets in each group, how many groups are there?

There are _____ _____ groups.
<u>at least/at most</u>

ISBN: 978-1-77149-206-5

⑧ Sweaters are on sale. Sasha buys 4 sweaters and spends less than $100. If the original price of each sweater is $38, what is the discount on each sweater?

_____

⑨ The average temperature of 3 cities is greater than -1°C. Two cities have the same temperature and one city is 5°C. What is the temperature of the two cities?

_____

⑩ Micah has 2 older siblings. His eldest brother is 1 year younger than 3 times his age and his middle brother is 5 years older than twice his age.

a. What is Micah's age?

_____

b. The sum of his brothers' ages is less than 44. What is Micah's exact age?

 Hints

Combine the inequalities from (a) and (b) to find Micah's exact age.

ISBN: 978-1-77149-206-5

⑪ A tennis court is a rectangle. Its width is 5 m and its length is x m longer.

   a. If the maximum area of the tennis court is 40 m², what is the length of the court?

Hints

Draw a diagram to help you visualize the problem.

   b. What is the perimeter of the court?

⑫ A train has a maximum capacity of 220 passengers, evenly distributed among a number of cabins. One trip had 4 empty cabins and the rest were full, while the return trip had fewer passengers, with 15 full cabins and 11 passengers in the remaining cabins.

   a. How many passengers could there be in each cabin?

   b. How many cabins does the train have?

ISBN: 978-1-77149-206-5

⑬ Andrea has the option of choosing Room A or B. Room B is bigger than Room A.

   a. What is the length of Room A?

   _____

   b. What is the difference in area if x is less than 15 m?

(x + 4) m

4 m   A

2 m

6 m   B   3 m

x m

_____

_____

⑭ Raymond is building identical towers with 30 blocks. Building 4 towers will leave at least 6 blocks and building 7 towers will require at least 5 more blocks. How many blocks are there in each tower?

_____

⑮ A factory specifies that each cotton swab must be between 50 and 60 mm long. 5 cotton swabs are taken as samples and their average length is less than 60 mm. If 3 swabs of equal lengths are 5 mm longer than the other 2 swabs, can it be certain that all the swabs pass the specifications?

_____

⑯ Aaron has $11.20 to buy doughnuts. If the average cost of a doughnut is more than $3.20, how many doughnuts can Aaron buy?

_____

ISBN: 978-1-77149-206-5

⑰
$-2(x + 8) + 20 > 0$ is the same as $-32 > -4(x + 10)$.

Susie

Is Susie correct?

_____

⑱ Daryl wanted to save $6000 over 5 years. However, after 5 years, he still had more than half to save. How much did he save each year?

_____

⑲ Goldilocks measured the temperatures of a few bowls of porridge. For the first bowl, she said, "This is too cold. It needs to be twice as hot." For the second bowl, she said, "This is too hot. It needs to be 8°C cooler." For the third one, she said, "This is just right. It is between 20°C and 24°C."

a. What was the temperature of the first bowl?

Tips

For an inequality that has 2 signs, break it into 2 inequalities first.

e.g.

$2 < 2x < 4$ → $\begin{array}{l} 2 < 2x \\ 2x < 4 \end{array}$

_____

b. What was the temperature of the second bowl?

_____

⑳ Mrs. Lowes wants to keep the grass on her lawn between 3 cm and 7 cm tall. The grass is currently 9 cm long and mowing it twice with her old lawnmower will cut the grass within that range. What length of grass is cut each time with the lawnmower?

_____

Graphs and Relations

solving a variety of word problems that involve graphing equations and slopes

 Math Skills

① Complete the tables with the given relations.

$y = x + 3$

x	y
0	
1	
2	

$y = 2x + (-1)$

x	y
-2	
0	
2	

$y = -x + 10$

x	y
-3	
-1	
1	

② Complete the relations with the given values.

$y = \boxed{}\, x + \boxed{}$

x	y
0	2
2	6
3	8

$y = \boxed{}\, x - \boxed{}$

x	y
0	-2
1	-1
5	3

$y = \boxed{}\, x + \boxed{}$

x	y
-3	9
0	3
4	-5

③ Find the slope of each line.

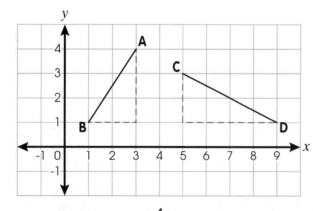

The slope of a line describes the direction and steepness of a line.

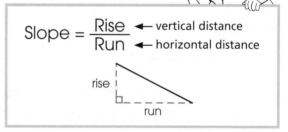

$$\text{Slope} = \frac{\text{Rise}}{\text{Run}} \quad \leftarrow \text{vertical distance} \\ \leftarrow \text{horizontal distance}$$

a. Slope of $\overline{AB}$ = $\dfrac{4 - }{3 - }$ = $\dfrac{}{}$

b. Compare the directions and steepness of the lines.

Slope of $\overline{CD}$ = $\dfrac{3 - }{5 - }$ = $-\dfrac{}{}$

_____

_____

ISBN: 978-1-77149-206-5

Problem Solving

The position of a sailboat has a relation of $y = 2x$. Complete the table of values and graph it. Use the graph to find the y-coordinate of the sailboat when x is 1.

Solution:

x	y
-1	
2	
3	

Step 1: To complete the table of values, find the values of y.

For $x = -1$, $y = 2 \times (-1)$

$y = \boxed{}$

For $x = 2$, $y = 2 \times \boxed{}$

$y = \boxed{}$

For $x = 3$, $y = 2 \times \boxed{}$

$y = \boxed{}$

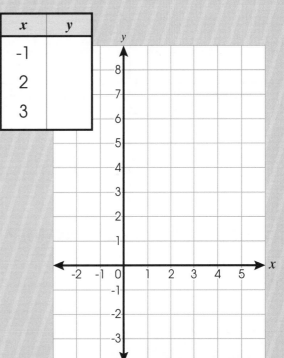

Step 2: Use the ordered pairs to graph the relation.

Ordered pairs:

$\boxed{}$, $\boxed{}$, $\boxed{}$

Step 3: Write a concluding sentence.

The y-coordinate of the sailboat is $\boxed{}$ when x is 1.

① Refer to the graph above. What is the

a. y-coordinate when x is 1.5?

_____

b. x-coordinate when y is 5?

_____

ISBN: 978-1-77149-206-5

② Alexandra drew 3 lines on the graph.

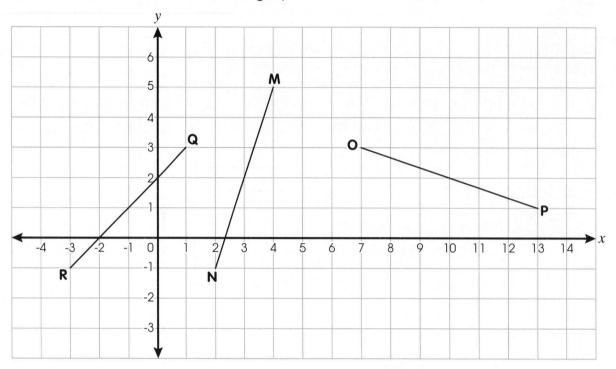

a. What is the slope of each line?

• Slope of $\overline{MN}$

_____

• Slope of $\overline{OP}$

_____

• Slope of $\overline{QR}$

_____

> **Tips**
>
> The order in which you subtract the points is not important, but you must subtract the x-coordinate in the same order as the y-coordinate.
>
> $$\text{Slope} = \frac{y_1 - y_2}{x_1 - x_2}$$
>
> coordinates of 1st point   coordinates of 2nd point

b. What does a slope with a negative value mean about a line?

_____

_____

c. What does a slope that has a greater positive value mean about a line?

_____

_____

ISBN: 978-1-77149-206-5

d.
Use the graph to find the *x*-coordinate of each line for *y* = 2.

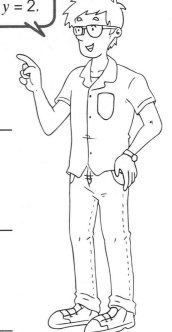

• $\overline{MN}$

_____

• $\overline{OP}$

_____

• $\overline{QR}$

_____

e. Alexandra says, "*y* = *x* + 3 is the relation that describes $\overline{QR}$." Is she correct?

Hints

Substitute the *x*-coordinate into the relation to find the *y*-coordinate.

_____

f. Which line does each relation describe?

• *y* = 3*x* − 7   • *y* = *x* + 2

_____   _____

③ Help the children graph the lines.

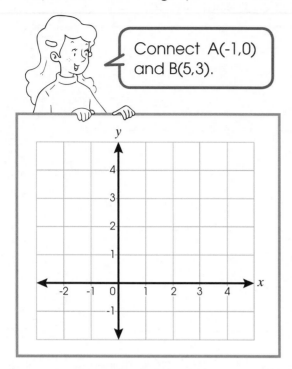

a. What is the slope?

_____

b. What is the *y*-coordinate when

   • *x* is 3?

   _____

   • *x* is 4?

   _____

c. What is the slope?

_____

d. What is the *x*-coordinate when

   • *y* is 0?

   _____

   • *y* is -2?

   _____

e. Which line is steeper?

_____

f. At which points do the lines touch the *x*-axis and the *y*-axis?

_____

_____

ISBN: 978-1-77149-206-5

④ Complete the tables of values for the following relations. Then graph them.

a. Line A:

$$y = -\frac{1}{3}x + 4\frac{2}{3}$$

x	y
-4	
-1	
5	

b. Line B:

$$y = 2x - 4$$

x	y
-1	
1	
3	

c. Line C:

$$y = 0.1x - 4.5$$

x	y
-5	
0	
5	

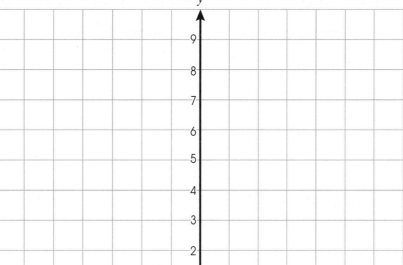
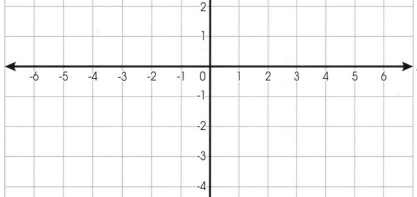

d. For Line A, what is the value of y when x is 1.2?

Hints

To find the exact value of y, substitute 1.2 for x in the relation.

_____

e. What is the slope of each line?

_____

ISBN: 978-1-77149-206-5

⑤ Mr. Duncan designed 2 escalators for a shopping mall.

a. Find the relation of y in terms of x for each escalator.

• Escalator A:

$2y + x = 12$

• Escalator B:

$2y + 4 = x$

Hints

Rearrange the terms to isolate y on the left hand side of the equations.

b. Both escalators run from $x = 2$ to $x = 14$. Find the end points of the escalators and graph them.

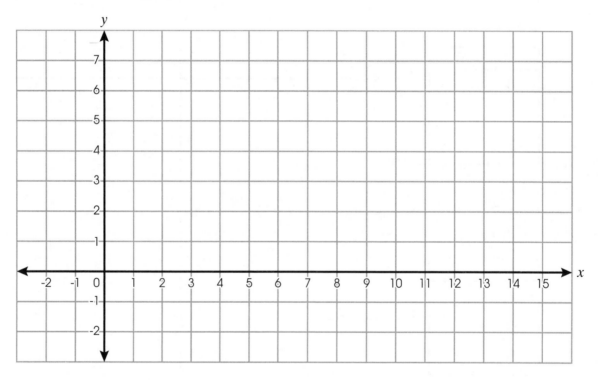

c. At which point do the escalators intersect?

_____

d. Find the slopes of the escalators. Compare their steepness and directions.

_____

_____

ISBN: 978-1-77149-206-5

⑥ A mountain trail is divided into 3 sections as
shown on the grid.

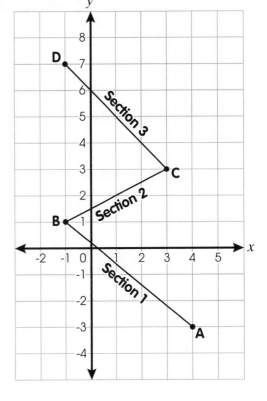

   a. What is the slope of each section? Which
      section has the steepest slope?

_____

   b. What would the slope have been if the
      trail went directly from Point A to Point D?

_____

_____

⑦ A cable car route is a straight line with end points at (-1,2) and (5,6).

   a. What is the slope of the route?

_____

   b. Does the relation $y = \frac{2}{3}x + 2\frac{2}{3}$ describe the route? If so, is the point
      $(3, 4\frac{2}{3})$ on the route?

_____

   c. There is a station at the midpoint of the
      route. What are the coordinates of the
      station?

 Hints

The midpoint is the same
distance from the end
points, both horizontally
and vertically.

_____

ISBN: 978-1-77149-206-5

Probability

solving a variety of word problems that involve finding probabilities of independent events and dependent events

 **Math Skills**

Independent Events

Two events are independent if the probability of the occurrence of one event _____ the probability of the other event.
affects/does not affect

Dependent Events

Two events are dependent if the occurrence of the first event _____ the probability of the second event.
affects/does not affect

① Determine whether each scenario involves independent events (IE) or dependent events (DE).

a.
- Pick a ball twice with replacement. Find the probability of picking 2 ⦾.

- Pick a ball twice without replacement. Find the probability of picking 2 ⦾.

b.
Toss the coin twice.

- Find the probability of getting 2 heads.

- Find the probability of getting a head on the first toss and a tail on the second toss.

c.
Spin the wheel twice.

A   A
C

- Find the probability of it landing on A on the first spin and C on the second spin.

- Find the probability of it landing on A on both spins.

- Find the probability of it landing on the same letter on both spins.

ISBN: 978-1-77149-206-5

Problem Solving

Jonathan has 2 blue and 3 red marbles, as well as 2 blue and 3 red clips. If he picks 1 marble and 1 clip at random, what is the probability of him picking a red marble and a blue clip?

Solution:

Step 1: **Determine whether they are independent or dependent events.**

> If two events do not affect the outcome of each other, they are considered independent events.

Think Does picking a marble affect the probability of picking a clip? If not, then they are independent events.

event A   event B

P(red marble and blue clip)

= P(red marble) × P(blue clip)

> For independent events A and B,
> **P(A and B) = P(A) × P(B)**

Step 2: **Find the probabilities.**

P(red marble) = ☐   P(blue clip) = ☐

P(red marble and blue clip) = ☐ × ☐ = ☐

Step 3: **Write a concluding sentence.**

The probability is ☐ .

① Refer to the question above. What is the probability of picking

   a. a blue marble and a red clip?   b. a red marble and a red clip?

   The probability is _____ .   The probability is _____ .

② Benson picks a ball twice with replacement and spins the spinner twice. Find the probabilities.

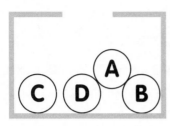

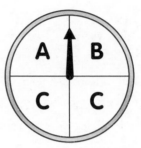

a. P(picking 2 A's)

_____

b. P(picking B and then D)

_____

c. P(picking 2 vowels)

_____

d. P(spinning A and then C)

_____

e. P(spinning a vowel and then a consonant)

_____

f. P(spinning 2 consonants)

_____

g.

> I will pick one ball and spin the spinner once.

Find the probabilities.

• P(picking B and spinning C)

_____

• P(picking a consonant and spinning a vowel)

_____

h. Are the events of picking and then spinning the same letter independent or dependent? Explain.

_____

_____

ISBN: 978-1-77149-206-5

③ Carlos has a red dice and a blue dice. He rolls both dice once.

a. Find the probabilities.

- P(1 on red and 6 on blue)

- P(2 on red and an even number on blue)

_____

- P(an odd number on both dice)

- P(5 or 6 on red and 1 on blue)

_____

b.

> I will find the sum of the numbers on both dice. Complete the table and find the probabilities.

- P(a sum of 10)

_____

- P(a sum less than 7)

+	1	2	3	4	5	6
1						
2						
3						
4						
5						
6						

_____

c. What is the average of the outcomes?

 Hints

"The average of the outcomes" can be considered the expected value.

$$\text{Expected value} = \frac{\text{sum of outcomes}}{\text{no. of outcomes}}$$

_____

ISBN: 978-1-77149-206-5

④ Ashley picks a card twice without replacement.

| 3 | K | E | 4 | D | 2 | 3 | E |

a. Are they independent events or dependent events? Explain.

_____

_____

_____

Tips

If one event affects the outcome of another event, then they are dependent events.

b. Find the probabilities.

• P(4 and then E)

Hints

After the first card is picked, only 7 cards are left.

_____

• P(two E's)

• P(a vowel and then a number)

_____   _____

• P(two K's)

• P(K and then 3)

_____   _____

c.

Ashley

If I pick a card three times, what is the probability that they will all be numbers?

_____

ISBN: 978-1-77149-206-5

⑤ Theo puts 5 green balls and 5 yellow balls into a box. He then picks 2 balls randomly without replacement.

a. Complete the tree diagram.

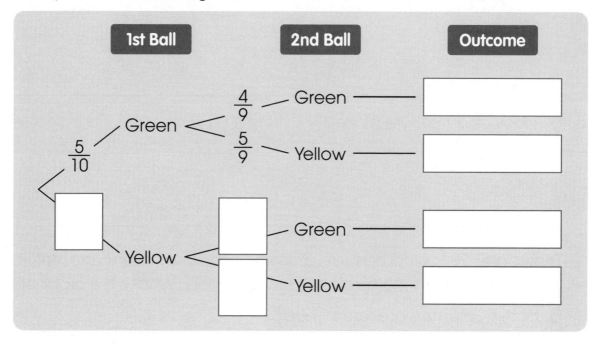

| 1st Ball | 2nd Ball | Outcome |

$\frac{5}{10}$ Green

$\frac{4}{9}$ Green

$\frac{5}{9}$ Yellow

Yellow

Green

Yellow

b. Find the probabilities.

• P(2 Green)

Hints

Multiply $\frac{5}{10}$ and $\frac{4}{9}$ from the tree diagram to find the answer.

_____

• P(1 Yellow, 1 Green)

• P(the same colour for both)

_____   _____

c. If Theo picks 3 balls without replacement instead, what is the probability that he will pick 3 green balls?

_____

ISBN: 978-1-77149-206-5

⑥ A class has 8 boys and 7 girls. Mr. Anson picks a group leader for Group A and then a group leader for Group B. What is the probability that

a. 2 boys are picked?

_____

b. 1 boy and 1 girl are picked?

_____

⑦ There are 25 computers at a store and 6 of them are refurbished. 2 computers are randomly picked for inspection. What is the probability that

a. both computers are refurbished?

_____

b. both computers are not refurbished?

_____

⑧ Mrs. Smith has 2 children. What is the probability that

a. she has 1 boy and 1 girl?

_____

b. the first child is a girl and the second child is a boy?

_____

ISBN: 978-1-77149-206-5

⑨ A bag has 10 red candies and 6 yellow candies. A box has 8 red candies and 8 yellow candies. Joshua picks 2 candies from the bag with replacement and Esther picks 2 candies from the box without replacement.

   a. Find the probabilities of Joshua and Esther picking

      • 1 red candy and 1 yellow candy.

_____

      • 2 yellow candies.

_____

   b. If both children picked a red candy on the first pick, whose probability of picking a yellow candy on the second pick is greater?

_____

⑩ Mariah has a regular deck of 52 cards. She draws two cards without replacement.

   a. What is the probability that both cards are ♥?

Hints

> In a regular deck of cards, there are 4 suits (♠,♥,♣,♦) with 13 cards each. Each card is also labelled with a number or letter, with 1 number or letter in each suit.

_____

   b. What is the probability that both cards are Q?

_____

   c. What is the probability that Mariah picks a Q♥ first and then another Q card?

_____

ISBN: 978-1-77149-206-5

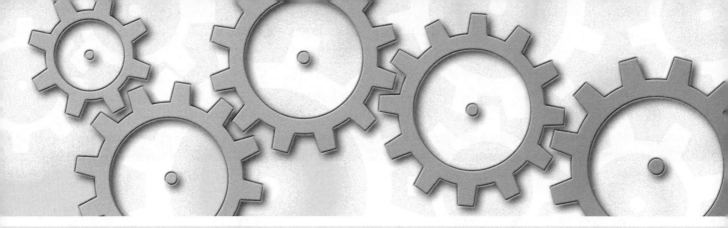

Section 2:
Critical-thinking Questions

ISBN: 978-1-77149-206-5

Critical-thinking Questions – **Level 1**

Students are required to solve multi-step questions which involve various topics in each.

Topics Covered

	Number Sense and Numeration	Measurement	Geometry and Spatial Sense	Patterning and Algebra	Data Management and Probability	My Record ✔ correct ✗ incorrect
1	decimals percents					
2	fractions				probability	
3	ratios	volume surface area		equations		
4	real numbers	circles	Pythagorean relationship			
5	proportions		angles			
6	percents			inequalities		
7	decimals			equations		
8		surface area	Pythagorean relationship			
9				equations relations		
10	rates			equations		
11			Cartesian coordinate plane	relations		
12			Pythagorean relationship Cartesian coordinate plane			
13			Pythagorean relationship angles/triangles			
14	ratios				probability	
15		circles		inequalities		
16				equations graphs		
17				graphs relations	data management	
18	percents	volume		polynomials		
19	fractions rates					
20		volume surface area	Pythagorean relationship			

114

ISBN: 978-1-77149-206-5

① Jason had a coupon that offered a discount in percent. It has saved $85.20 on a guitar, which now costs $482.80. If the coupon were used to save $39.60 on a harmonica, how much would the harmonica cost after the discount?

Percent discount: $\dfrac{\rule{3cm}{0.4pt}}{(\rule{1cm}{0.4pt} + \rule{1cm}{0.4pt})}$ = _____ = _____%

Original price of harmonica: _____ ÷ _____ = _____

Discounted price of harmonica: _____ − _____ = _____

The harmonica would cost _____ .

② Christine has a bag with 25 candies. $\dfrac{1}{5}$ of them are green, $\dfrac{2}{5}$ of the remaining are red, and the rest are yellow. If she eats 2 candies in a row, what is the probability that the first candy is green and the second candy is yellow?

③ The ratio of a cylindrical container's diameter to its height is 2:1. If the surface area of the container is 1256 cm², what is the volume of the container?

Topics covered:

Question 1
- decimals
- percents

Question 2
- fractions
- probability

Question 3
- ratios
- volume
- surface area
- equations

ISBN: 978-1-77149-206-5

④ A toy barrel rolls down a ramp as shown and makes exactly 4 rotations. What is the radius of the barrel in centimetres?

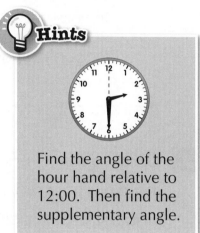

2^{-1} m

$\sqrt{2}$ m

⑤ What is the measure of the obtuse angle between the hour hand and the minute hand when it is 2:30?

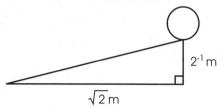

Hints

Find the angle of the hour hand relative to 12:00. Then find the supplementary angle.

⑥ Anna's skating team has won 60% of the 30 competitions in which they have competed. If they need a record of at least 70% wins to make the finals, how many of the remaining 20 competitions must they win?

⑦ Nate flies a remote control airplane where its height in h metres after t seconds is modelled by $h = t^3$. What is the difference in height between 4.5 s and 5 s?

Topics covered:

Question 4	**Question 5**	**Question 6**	**Question 7**
• real numbers	• proportions	• percents	• decimals
• Pythagorean relationship	• angles	• inequalities	• equations
• circles			

ISBN: 978-1-77149-206-5

⑧ The base of the triangular prism shown is an equilateral triangle. What is the surface area of the prism?

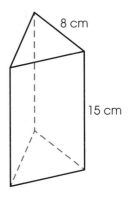

⑨ Turtle Danny walks 11 m in 1 min, 19 m in 2 min, and 27 m in 3 min. Write an equation to describe the relationship between the distance and time. If he continues at the same pace, will he have walked 80 m after 10 min?

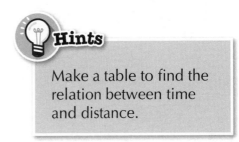

Hints

Make a table to find the relation between time and distance.

⑩ Refer to Question 9. Turtle Sandra walks 30 m in 2.5 min. She is 25 m behind Turtle Danny when they start. If they start walking at the same time, how long will it take Turtle Sandra to catch up to Turtle Danny?

Topics covered:

Question 8	Question 9	Question 10
• Pythagorean relationship	• equations	• rates
• surface area	• relations	• equations

ISBN: 978-1-77149-206-5

⑪ The top of a ski lift is located at (-3,2). The coordinates of the bottom of the ski lift are 3 units down and 2 units to the right from the top, and then reflected in the y-axis. What is the slope of the ski lift?

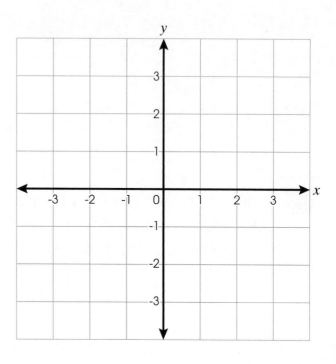

⑫ Refer to Question 11. The distance between the bottom of the ski lift and (1,-3) is 0.2 km. What is the length of the ski lift?

Topics covered:

Question 11
- Cartesian coordinate plane
- relations

Question 12
- Pythagorean relationship
- Cartesian coordinate plane

ISBN: 978-1-77149-206-5

⑬ Are △ABC and △DCE congruent?

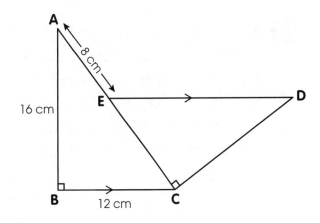

⑭ In a bag, there are 8 green marbles for every 3 red marbles. There is also 1 blue marble for every 2 red marbles. If there are 32 green marbles, what is the probability of picking 2 blue marbles in a row without replacement?

⑮ Paula wants to draw a circle that has an area between 113.04 cm² and 78.5 cm². What is the range of the possible circumferences?

Topics covered:

Question 13
- Pythagorean relationship
- angles
- triangles

Question 14
- ratios
- probability

Question 15
- circles
- inequalities

ISBN: 978-1-77149-206-5

May's and Dawn's savings over 8 weeks are described by the relations below, where x represents the number of weeks and y represents the amount of savings.

May: $y = 8 - x$

Dawn: $y = 2x - 2$

Graph the relations. How much more savings did Dawn have than May in Week 7?

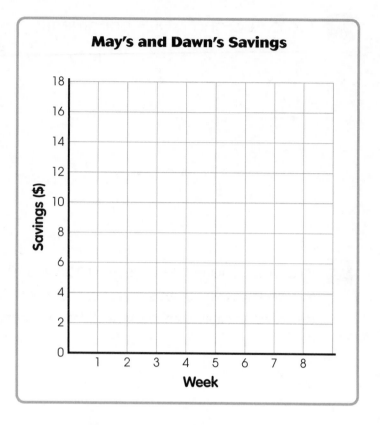

May's and Dawn's Savings

Savings ($) vs Week

⑰ Refer to Question 16. Serena had the same amount of savings as May in Week 2 and as Dawn in Week 6. Write an equation to describe Serena's savings and graph it. How much did she have in Week 8?

Topics covered:

Question 16
- equations
- graphs

Question 17
- graphs
- relations
- data management

ISBN: 978-1-77149-206-5

⑱ Donna takes a cube and cuts out the largest cylinder possible. What percent of the cube's volume is cut out?

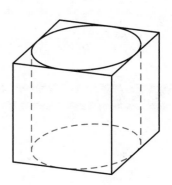

⑲ Jason can peel 15 potatoes in 25 minutes. Janette can peel 8 potatoes in $\frac{1}{10}$ hour. If they start peeling potatoes at the same time, how many minutes will it take them to peel 406 potatoes?

⑳ A square-based pyramid has a height of 12 cm. If the base of the pyramid is 100 cm², what are the surface area and volume of the pyramid?

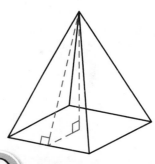

Hints

Use the Pythagorean relationship to find the height of each triangular face.

Topics covered:

Question 18
- percents
- volume
- polynomials

Question 19
- fractions
- rates

Question 20
- Pythagorean relationship
- volume
- surface area

ISBN: 978-1-77149-206-5

Students are required to solve multi-step questions which involve various topics in each.

Topics Covered

	Number Sense and Numeration	Measurement	Geometry and Spatial Sense	Patterning and Algebra	Data Management and Probability	My Record ✔ correct ✘ incorrect
1	decimals	volume				☐
2		circles	Pythagorean relationship			☐
3	percents			inequalities		☐
4	fractions/rates decimals					☐
5	real numbers	volume		equations		☐
6	ratios	circles		polynomials	probability	☐
7		volume surface area	Pythagorean relationship			☐
8	proportions		Pythagorean relationship			☐
9				polynomials	probability	☐
10	percents	surface area				☐
11			Cartesian coordinate plane	graphs relations		☐
12			Cartesian coordinate plane	graphs relations		☐
13	ratios	volume surface area				☐
14	fractions percents					☐
15			Pythagorean relationship	equations		☐
16	real numbers	volume		inequalities		☐
17		circles volume		equations		☐
18		surface area	Pythagorean relationship			☐
19	fractions rates					☐
20			angles	equations		☐

ISBN: 978-1-77149-206-5

① A cone with a radius of 9 cm and a height of 12.5 cm is filled with water. The water is then poured to fill a rectangular tank with a length of 7.5 cm and a width of 6 cm. What is the water level of the tank?

Volume of water: $\frac{1}{3}$ × 3.14 × _____² × _____ = _____

Water level: _____ ÷ _____ ÷ _____ = _____

The water level is _____ .

② The vertices of the triangle are at the centres of the circles as shown. The circumference of each circle is 28.26 cm. What is the area of the triangle?

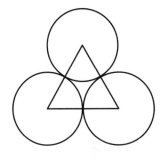

③ Marco's hockey team has lost 15% of their 20 games so far. If his team wants a record of at least 75% wins, how many of their remaining 16 games do they need to win?

Topics covered:

Question 1
- decimals
- volume

Question 2
- circles
- Pythagorean relationship

Question 3
- percents
- inequalities

ISBN: 978-1-77149-206-5

④ A truck consumes 4.65 L of gas for $40\frac{1}{10}$ km. A van consumes $4\frac{1}{2}$ L for 40 km. Which vehicle is more gas efficient?

⑤ A stack of 6 identical cube-shaped boxes has a volume of 3.84×10^5 cm³. What is the side length of each box?

⑥ Two circles form a target. The ratio of the two circles' radii is 3:1. What is the probability of hitting the shaded area twice in a row?

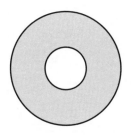

⑦ The surface area of a cone with a radius of 8 cm is 628 cm². What is its volume?

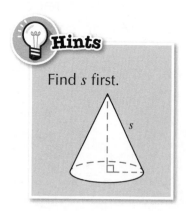

Hints

Find *s* first.

Topics covered:

Question 4	**Question 5**	**Question 6**	**Question 7**
• fractions	• real numbers	• ratios	• Pythagorean relationship
• decimals	• volume	• circles	• volume
• rates	• equations	• polynomials	• surface area
		• probability	

ISBN: 978-1-77149-206-5

⑧ The side lengths of △ABC and △DEC are proportional. What are their perimeters?

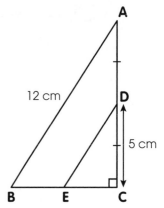

⑨ Ada has a deck of $4n^4$ cards. $2n^2$ of them are white cards and the rest are black cards. If she draws 2 cards randomly without replacement, what is the probability that she will draw 2 white cards in a row?

Hints

Write the answer as a polynomial. Simplify as much as possible.

⑩ The radius of a ball increased from 8 cm to 10 cm. How much did its surface area increase in percent?

Topics covered:

Question 8
- proportions
- Pythagorean relationship

Question 9
- polynomials
- probability

Question 10
- percents
- surface area

ISBN: 978-1-77149-206-5

⑪ Andrea's house is at (0,1) and her grandma's is at (3,4). A bike lane runs across the grid in a straight line, connecting both houses. Draw the line. Write an equation to describe the relation between the x- and y-coordinates of the bike lane.

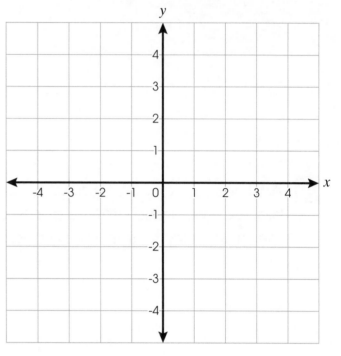

⑫ Refer to Question 11. A bus route is the reflection of the bike lane in the x-axis and the translation of 2 units to the left. Write an equation to describe the relation of the x- and y-coordinates of the bus route. At which point do the bus route and the bike lane intersect?

Take 2 points from the bike lane and perform the transformations. Then connect the transformed points to find the bus route.

Topics covered:

Question 11
- Cartesian coordinate plane
- graphs
- relations

Question 12
- Cartesian coordinate plane
- graphs
- relations

ISBN: 978-1-77149-206-5

⑬ Two cylinders are as shown. The ratio of their radii is 2:1. What are the ratios of their volumes and surface areas?

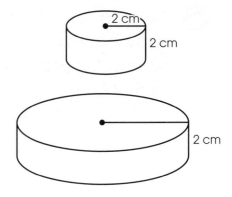

⑭ Arnold's earnings was $54 000 last year. He paid an income tax of 15% on the first $\frac{5}{6}$ of his earnings and 20% on the rest. How much money did Arnold make after tax last year?

⑮ Tara draws a right triangle that has the same base and height. She then draws another right triangle where the base is 3 cm shorter and the height is 4 times as long. If the areas of both triangles are the same, what is the difference in their perimeters?

Topics covered:

Question 13
- ratios
- volume
- surface area

Question 14
- fractions
- percents

Question 15
- Pythagorean relationship
- equations

ISBN: 978-1-77149-206-5

The area of the base of Maggie's wooden cube was x cm². She cut out a new cube from it with a side length that is 5 cm shorter. If the new cube has a volume of at least 64 cm³, what was the area of the base of the original cube?

⑰ Kyle has a toy ice cream that is made up of a cone and half of a sphere. If the diameter of the sphere is 6 cm and the volume of the toy is 150.72 cm³, what is the total height of the toy?

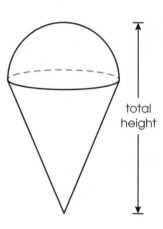

total height

Topics covered:

Question 16
- real numbers
- volume
- inequalities

Question 17
- circles
- volume
- equations

ISBN: 978-1-77149-206-5

⑱ The base of a triangular prism is an equilateral triangle with side lengths of 5.8 cm. The height of the prism is 20 cm. What is the surface area of the prism?

⑲ Amy assembles 5 chairs in $1\frac{3}{4}$ h and Ben assembles 7 chairs in $1\frac{2}{5}$ h. What is the difference in their rates in h/chair? What is their difference in the number of hours needed to assemble 3 chairs?

⑳ What is ∠BCD if ∠BDE is $\frac{46x + 28}{0.4x}$ and ∠AED is $\frac{16x - 3}{0.4x}$?

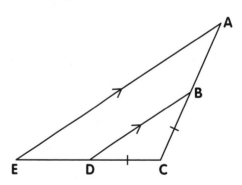

Topics covered:

Question 18	**Question 19**	**Question 20**
• Pythagorean relationship	• fractions	• angles
• surface area	• rates	• equations

ISBN: 978-1-77149-206-5

Critical-thinking Questions – Level 1

Students are required to solve multi-step questions which involve various topics in each.

Topics Covered

	Number Sense and Numeration	Measurement	Geometry and Spatial Sense	Patterning and Algebra	Data Management and Probability	My Record ✔ correct ✘ incorrect
1	percents	volume				
2	ratios				probability	
3	real numbers		Pythagorean relationship			
4	decimals percents					
5	fractions	circles		equations		
6	rates	surface area				
7			angles triangles		probability	
8	rates proportions			polynomials		
9		surface area	Pythagorean relationship			
10	ratios	volume surface area		equations		
11	ratios		angles triangles	equations		
12		circles	Pythagorean relationship			
13	rates	surface area				
14			Cartesian coordinate plane	graphs relations		
15			Pythagorean relationship Cartesian coordinate plane			
16	real numbers			equations		
17	fractions percents					
18	real numbers			inequalities	probability	
19	proportions	circles	angles triangles			
20		volume surface area		equations		

ISBN: 978-1-77149-206-5

① Cylinder A has a radius of 3 cm and a height of 8 cm and is full of water. Cylinder B has a radius of 4 cm and a height of 9 cm. If the water in Cylinder A is poured into Cylinder B, what percent of Cylinder B is filled with water?

Volume of Cylinder A: $3.14 \times$ _____ $^2 \times$ _____ = _____

Volume of Cylinder B: $3.14 \times$ _____ $^2 \times$ _____ = _____

Percent filled: _____ ÷ _____ × 100% = _____

_____ of Cylinder B is filled.

② The ratio of red balls to green balls in a box is 1:4. Anita picked 2 balls from the box and the probability that both balls were red was less than 4%. Was the first ball replaced before she picked the second ball?

③ Ryu put 3 right triangles together to make a design. What are the area and perimeter of the design?

Topics covered:

Question 1
- percents
- volume

Question 2
- ratios
- probability

Question 3
- real numbers
- Pythagorean relationship

ISBN: 978-1-77149-206-5

④ The price of potato soup increased from $6.75 to $7.83. If the price of a chicken pot pie increased by the same percent to $18.85, what was the original price of the chicken pot pie?

⑤ Venisa cut out part of a circle to make the shape shown. The area of the shape is 94.2 cm². What is a?

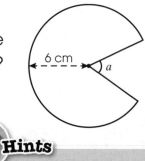

6 cm

a

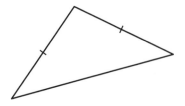

Hints

The area of the cut-out is proportional to the measure of Angle a.

⑥ Tori needs to paint a cylinder with a radius of 10 cm and a height of 8 cm. If Tori paints at a rate of 1.875 cm²/s, how many minutes will it take her to paint 3 coats?

⑦ Esme draws an angle bisector to divide the triangle shown into 2 triangles. What is the probability that the 2 new triangles are congruent?

Topics covered:

Question 4	Question 5	Question 6	Question 7
• decimals	• fractions	• rates	• angles
• percents	• circles	• surface area	• triangles
	• equations		• probability

ISBN: 978-1-77149-206-5

⑧ John walked $2x^3$ metres in $4x^2$ seconds. If he continues at the same speed to walk $8x$ metres more, he will have walked a total of 80 seconds. What was John's speed?

⑨ Shaun's cone has a radius of 6 cm and a surface area of 301.44 cm³. If he cuts the cone into 2 equal halves, what is the surface area of each half?

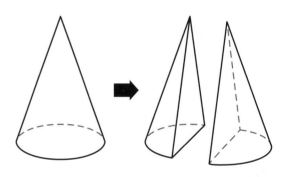

⑩ The ratio of the length to width to height of a rectangular prism is 3:2:5 and its volume is 3750 cm³. What is its surface area?

Topics covered:

Question 8	**Question 9**	**Question 10**
• rates	• Pythagorean relationship	• ratios
• proportions	• surface area	• volume
• polynomials		• surface area
		• equations

ISBN: 978-1-77149-206-5

⑪ Two triangles are similar if their corresponding angles are equal. Are △ABC and △CDE similar? If so, what is the length of $\overline{AB}$?

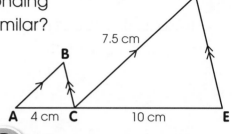

7.5 cm

A　4 cm　C　　　10 cm　　　E

Hints

In similar triangles, the ratios of their corresponding sides are the same.

⑫ Two identical squares are placed inside a circle. The circle has a radius of 5 cm. What is the area of the circle not covered by the squares?

⑬ Virgil is painting with a paint roller that has a radius of 3 cm and a width of 10 cm. What is the rate in rotations/min if he finishes painting an area of 30 000 cm² in 4 minutes?

10 cm

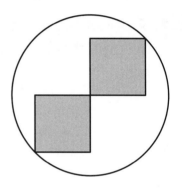

Topics covered:

Question 11
- ratios
- angles
- triangles
- equations

Question 12
- Pythagorean relationship
- circles

Question 13
- rates
- surface area

ISBN: 978-1-77149-206-5

⑭ Below are the relations of 3 lines. Their intersections are the vertices of a triangular field. What are the coordinates of each vertex?

Lines: $y = -\dfrac{1}{2}x + 2$

$y = -2x - 1$

$y = x - 1$

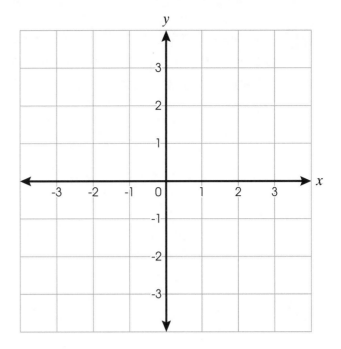

⑮ Refer to Question 14. If the side length of each square on the grid is 5 m, what is the perimeter of the field?

Topics covered:

Question 14
- Cartesian coordinate plane
- graphs
- relations

Question 15
- Pythagorean relationship
- Cartesian coordinate plane

ISBN: 978-1-77149-206-5

Jacob is thinking of four integers. The sum of the squares of two integers is equal to the sum of the squares of the other two integers. If three of the integers are 3, 7, and 9, what is the last integer?

You will need to test all 3 possible combinations.

⑰ Stanley had $3\frac{1}{3}$ L of juice and $1\frac{3}{4}$ L of it is consumed. How much of the juice is consumed in percent?

⑱ Tina has an integer in mind. She will get at most 7 if she subtracts 4 from it and she will get at least -17 if she adds -25 to it. What is the probability that the integer is divisible by 3?

Set up 2 inequalities.

Topics covered:

Question 16	**Question 17**	**Question 18**
• real numbers	• fractions	• real numbers
• equations	• percents	• inequalities
		• probability

ISBN: 978-1-77149-206-5

⑲ Point B is the centre of the circle shown. Are △ABC and △DEF congruent?

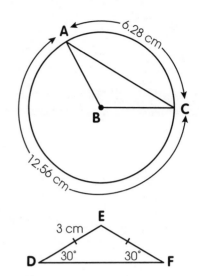

Hints

The length of an arc is proportional to the size of the angle.

⑳ The largest sphere inside a cube is cut out and a volume of $822\frac{6}{7}$ cm³ remains. What is the surface area of the sphere? (Use $\pi = \frac{22}{7}$.)

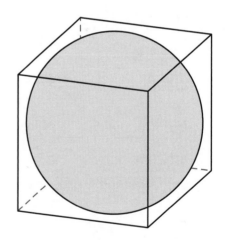

Topics covered:

Question 19
- proportions
- circles
- angles
- triangles

Question 20
- volume
- surface area
- equations

ISBN: 978-1-77149-206-5

Students are required to solve multi-step questions which involve various topics in each.

Topics Covered

	Number Sense and Numeration	Measurement	Geometry and Spatial Sense	Patterning and Algebra	Data Management and Probability	My Record
1	rates		Pythagorean relationship			
2	fractions		Cartesian coordinate plane	relations		
3	decimals			inequalities		
4	real numbers	circles				
5				equations	probability	
6		volume		equations		
7	ratios		angles	equations		
8		surface area	Pythagorean relationship			
9	proportions		triangles			
10	decimals			polynomials		
11	decimals	volume surface area				
12	percents	volume		equations		
13	decimals				probability	
14		circles		inequalities		
15	fractions percents					
16			Cartesian coordinate plane	equations graphs/relations		
17			Pythagorean relationship Cartesian coordinate plane			
18	decimals	volume				
19	fractions			inequalities		
20	real numbers ratios					

My Record: ✔ correct ✘ incorrect

ISBN: 978-1-77149-206-5

① Janette's house is 77 m west of Jason's house and 36 m north of Ainsley's house. If Ainsley walks in a straight line from her house to Jason's house at a speed of 1.7 m/s, how long will it take Ainsley?

Distance to Jason's house: $\sqrt{\underline{\hspace{1.5cm}}^2 + \underline{\hspace{1.5cm}}^2} = \underline{\hspace{2cm}}$

Time taken: $\underline{\hspace{1.5cm}} \div \underline{\hspace{1.5cm}} = \underline{\hspace{2cm}}$

It will take Ainsley $\underline{\hspace{2cm}}$.

② Point S is at $(-1\frac{1}{2}, 6\frac{1}{2})$. Point T is the image of Point S. It was translated $2\frac{1}{2}$ units to the right and $9\frac{1}{2}$ units down, and then reflected in the y-axis. What is the slope of $\overline{ST}$?

③ Frederick is saving money to buy a book series. Each week, he gets $20 for allowance but spends $4.25 on candies. There are 5 books in the series and each book costs $18.90. At least how many weeks does Frederick need to save to buy all the books in the series?

Topics covered:

Question 1
- rates
- Pythagorean relationship

Question 2
- fractions
- Cartesian coordinate plane
- relations

Question 3
- decimals
- inequalities

ISBN: 978-1-77149-206-5

④ The square shown has an area of 20.5 cm². What is the area of the circle?

Hints

Keep numbers as square roots until the end.

⑤ Annie has 5 cards. She picks 2 cards at random with replacement. The probability that she will pick 2 red cards is $\frac{4}{25}$. How many red cards are there?

⑥ Thomas reshapes a cube-shaped block of clay with a volume of 216 cm³ into a square-based pyramid that has the same base as the cube. How much taller is the pyramid than the cube?

⑦ What is the ratio of $x:y$?

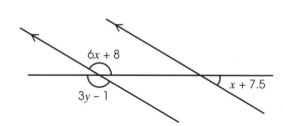

6x + 8

3y − 1

x + 7.5

Topics covered:

Question 4	**Question 5**	**Question 6**	**Question 7**
• real numbers	• equations	• volume	• ratios
• circles	• probability	• equations	• angles
			• equations

ISBN: 978-1-77149-206-5

⑧ Riley cut a cylinder into a cone with the same radius and height. The cylinder had a radius of 6 cm and a height of 8 cm. What is the change in surface area?

⑨ △ABC and △DEF are similar triangles. Are △DEF and △IHG congruent?

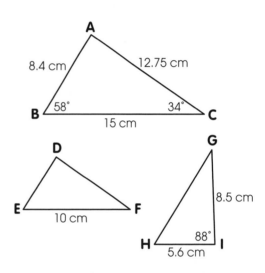

⑩ Gary threw a tennis ball into the air. The ball reached a height of $6t - t^2$ metres, where t was the time in seconds that the ball remained in the air. When was the ball higher, at 1.4 seconds or 4.7 seconds?

Topics covered:

Question 8	**Question 9**	**Question 10**
• surface area	• proportions	• decimals
• Pythagorean relationship	• triangles	• polynomials

ISBN: 978-1-77149-206-5

⑪ Maria's pencil is composed of half a sphere, a cylinder, and a cone. What are the volume and surface area of the pencil?

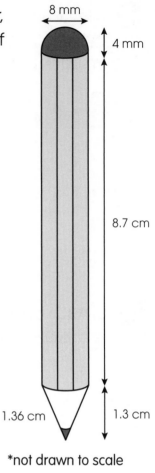

8 mm

4 mm

8.7 cm

1.36 cm

1.3 cm

*not drawn to scale

⑫ Refer to Question 11. As Maria uses her pencil, the length of the cylinder decreases. If the volume of Maria's pencil decreases by 20%, how long will her pencil be?

Topics covered:

Question 11
- decimals
- volume
- surface area

Question 12
- percents
- volume
- equations

ISBN: 978-1-77149-206-5

⑬ Steven is playing a game where 0.1 of the outcomes are wins, 0.3 are draws, and the rest are losses. If he plays the game twice, what is the probability of him getting at least 1 win?

⑭ The circumference of a circle is greater than 47.1 cm. What is the area of the circle?

⑮ Shonda had $3\frac{1}{3}$ L of apple cider. The amount has decreased by 45% after she spilled some of it. What amount of apple cider remains?

Topics covered:

Question 13	Question 14	Question 15
• decimals	• circles	• fractions
• probability	• inequalities	• percents

ISBN: 978-1-77149-206-5

⑯ Kenny lives at (-3,4). His street is a straight line with a slope of $-1\frac{1}{2}$. If Mavis lives on the same street at an x-coordinate of 3, what is her y-coordinate?

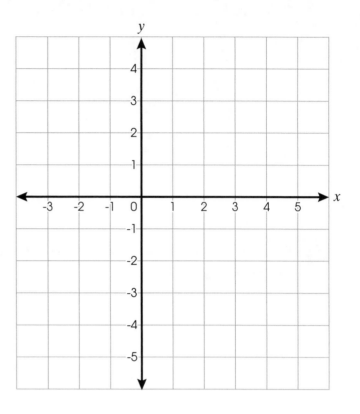

⑰ Refer to Question 16. Kenny and Mavis live 541 m apart. Robert lives at (4,2). Who lives closer to Robert and by how much?

Topics covered:

Question 16
- Cartesian coordinate plane
- equations
- graphs
- relations

Question 17
- Pythagorean relationship
- Cartesian coordinate plane

ISBN: 978-1-77149-206-5

⑱ The diameter of a glass cylinder is 10 cm. If a ball with a radius of 3 cm is submerged in the cylinder filled with water, by how much will the water level rise?

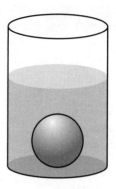

⑲ Leslie has a fruitcake and a cheesecake. The fruitcake weighs $2\frac{1}{10}$ kg. Leslie has eaten $\frac{1}{4}$ of the cheesecake and the total weight of the remaining cakes is less than $4\frac{1}{2}$ kg. How much did the cheesecake weigh?

⑳ In a town with a population of 1.2×10^5, the ratio of people to doctors is 3000:7. How many doctors are there in the town?

Topics covered:

Question 18	Question 19	Question 20
• decimals	• fractions	• real numbers
• volume	• inequalities	• ratios

Students are required to solve multi-step questions which involve various topics in each.

Topics Covered

	Number Sense and Numeration	Measurement	Geometry and Spatial Sense	Patterning and Algebra	Data Management and Probability	My Record
						✔ correct ✘ incorrect
1	decimals percents					☐
2			Pythagorean relationship	polynomials		☐
3		circles	Pythagorean relationship			☐
4	percents				probability	☐
5			angles	equations		☐
6	fractions	volume				☐
7	percents	surface area		equations		☐
8	ratios		angles			☐
9		circles		inequalities		☐
10	ratios			equations	probability	☐
11			Pythagorean relationship triangles Cartesian coordinate plane			☐
12			Cartesian coordinate plane	graphs relations		☐
13	real numbers	volume surface area				☐
14	decimals rates			equations		☐
15	fractions		Pythagorean relationship			☐
16			Cartesian coordinate plane	graphs relations		☐
17			Cartesian coordinate plane	graphs relations		☐
18		circles	Pythagorean relationship			☐
19	percents rates			inequalities		☐
20	decimals	surface area	Pythagorean relationship			☐

ISBN: 978-1-77149-206-5

① Company A sells a $1029 phone at 15% off, while Company B sells the phone for $34.25 cheaper than the discounted price of Company A after a 12% discount. How much did Company B sell the phone for originally?

Discounted price at Company A: _____ × (1 – _____) = _____

Discounted price at Company B: _____ – _____ = _____

Original price at Company B: _____ ÷ (1 – _____) = _____

Company B sold the phone for _____ originally.

② Find a polynomial that describes the area of an equilateral triangle with a side length of s. Keep the numbers as square roots.

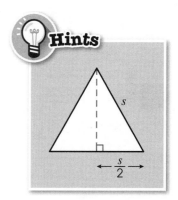

Hints

③ A coaster has a regular hexagon where each vertex lies on the edge of the circle as shown. If the coaster has a diameter of 8 cm, what is the area of the shaded part?

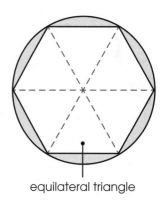

equilateral triangle

Topics covered:

Question 1	**Question 2**	**Question 3**
• decimals	• Pythagorean relationship	• circles
• percents	• polynomials	• Pythagorean relationship

ISBN: 978-1-77149-206-5

④ In a studio audience of 400 people, 85.75% are adults. If 2 members of the audience are picked at random, what is the probability that they are both children?

⑤ What is the value of x?

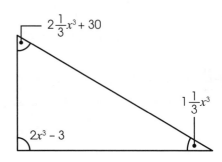

$2\frac{1}{3}x^3 + 30$

$1\frac{1}{3}x^3$

$2x^3 - 3$

⑥ How much water in millimetres can be added if the cylindrical glass is $\frac{2}{3}$ full?

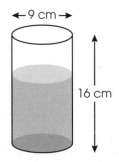

←9 cm→

16 cm

⑦ A spherical sponge has a diameter of 10 cm. When soaked, its surface area increases by 44%. What is the diameter of the sponge when soaked?

Topics covered:

Question 4	**Question 5**	**Question 6**	**Question 7**
• percents	• angles	• fractions	• percents
• probability	• equations	• volume	• surface area
			• equations

ISBN: 978-1-77149-206-5

⑧   Are △ABC and △CDE similar? If so, what is the ratio of the corresponding side lengths of △ABC and △CDE? What are the values of x and y?

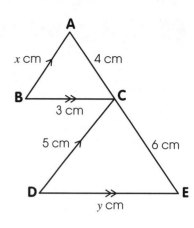

⑨   A window is in the shape of a semicircle and has an area greater than 0.98 m². What is the diameter of the window?

⑩   The ratio of winning balls to all balls in a bag is 3:8. If the probability of drawing 2 non-winning balls in a row is $\frac{5}{14}$, what is the ratio of non-winning balls to all balls after the first ball is drawn?

Topics covered:

Question 8	**Question 9**	**Question 10**
• ratios	• circles	• ratios
• angles	• inequalities	• equations
		• probability

Are △ABC and △DEF congruent?

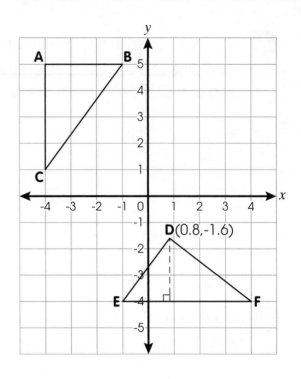

⑫ Refer to Question 11. Allison drew a line that has the same slope as $\overline{BC}$ and passes through (0,0). Write an equation to describe the line.

Topics covered:

Question 11
- Pythagorean relationship
- triangles
- Cartesian coordinate plane

Question 12
- Cartesian coordinate plane
- graphs
- relations

ISBN: 978-1-77149-206-5

⑬ The Earth has a diameter of about 1.3×10^4 km. If the Earth were a perfect sphere, what would its volume and surface area be? Write the answers in scientific notation.

⑭ Carol and Theresa are 525 m apart and they run toward each other. Carol runs at a speed of 6.2 m/s and Theresa runs at 4.3 m/s. How much farther will Carol have run than Theresa when they reach each other?

⑮ Is the shape inside the square shown an equilateral triangle? What fraction of the square's area does it take up?

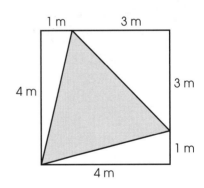

Topics covered:

Question 13	**Question 14**	**Question 15**
• real numbers	• decimals	• fractions
• volume	• rates	• Pythagorean relationship
• surface area	• equations	

ISBN: 978-1-77149-206-5

⑯ A pair of railroads are represented by Lines A and B on the grid. A new line, Line C, is planned. It is parallel to Line B and intersects Line A at (-2,-2). Draw the line and write its equation.

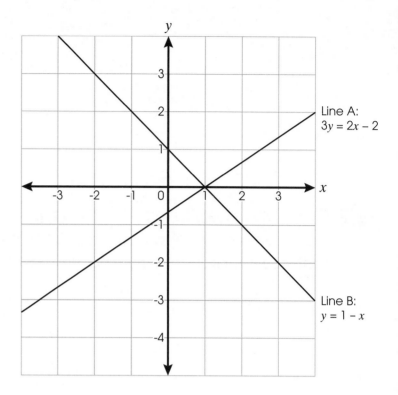

Line A:
$3y = 2x - 2$

Line B:
$y = 1 - x$

⑰ Refer to Question 16. Another railroad, Line D, meets Line B at (-1,2) and is perpendicular to it. What is the slope of Line D?

Topics covered:

Question 16
- Cartesian coordinate plane
- graphs
- relations

Question 17
- Cartesian coordinate plane
- graphs
- relations

ISBN: 978-1-77149-206-5

⑱ Points A, B, and C are the centres of the circles with circumferences of 25.12 cm, 31.4 cm, and 15.7 cm respectively.   What is the distance between Points A and C?

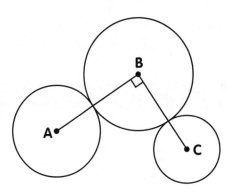

⑲ Lisa is organizing an annual charity show. Last year, she raised $2500 by selling 625 tickets. If she wants to raise at least $125 more than last year while selling 16% fewer tickets, what should the sales price be in $/ticket?

⑳ Miriam has taped two identical cones together to make a top. If she wants to paint the surface, what is the total area that needs to be painted?

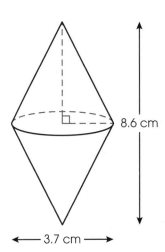

8.6 cm

←— 3.7 cm —→

Topics covered:

Question 18
• circles
• Pythagorean relationship

Question 19
• percents
• rates
• inequalities

Question 20
• decimals
• Pythagorean relationship
• surface area

ISBN: 978-1-77149-206-5

Students are required to solve multi-step questions which involve various topics in each.

Topics Covered

	Number Sense and Numeration	Measurement	Geometry and Spatial Sense	Patterning and Algebra	Data Management and Probability	My Record ✔ correct ✗ incorrect
1	fractions ratios		angles			☐
2			angles		probability	☐
3	decimals percents					☐
4	percents	volume surface area				☐
5			angles triangles	inequalities		☐
6	decimals rates		Pythagorean relationship			☐
7	ratios	volume		polynomials		☐
8	real numbers ratios	circles				☐
9	decimals		Cartesian coordinate plane	graphs		☐
10		volume	angles			☐
11	proportions	surface area				☐
12	ratios				probability	☐
13	fractions			polynomials equations		☐
14	fractions			inequalities		☐
15	decimals rates					☐
16			Pythagorean relationship Cartesian coordinate plane	graphs		☐
17	ratios				probability	☐
18	decimals rates		Pythagorean relationship			☐
19	decimals percents					☐
20	decimals rates					☐

ISBN: 978-1-77149-206-5

① What is the ratio between the acute angle and the reflex angle that the hour hand and the minute hand make at 8:30?

② Noella spins the spinner twice. What is the probability that she will get red on the first spin and green on the second spin?

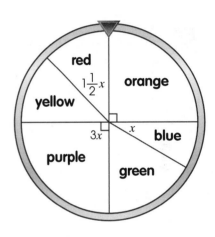

③ The price of a $593.20 watch is marked up by 105% and then discounted at 15%. After a 13% tax, how much is the watch?

Topics covered:

Question 1
- fractions
- ratios
- angles

Question 2
- angles
- probability

Question 3
- decimals
- percents

④ The side length of a cube was increased by 25%. If the volume of the new cube is 125 000 000 cm³, what was the surface area of the original cube in m²?

⑤ One of the angles in an obtuse triangle is $(2x + 6)°$. What can the value of x be?

⑥ The airport is 34 km south of Ivy's house. Clara's house is 8 km west of Ivy's house. Ivy's mom drove to Clara's house. She then drove southeast to drop the girls off at the airport and then drove back home. How far did she travel in all? If she drove at 60 km/h, how long did the entire trip take?

Topics covered:

Question 4	**Question 5**	**Question 6**
• percents	• angles	• decimals
• volume	• triangles	• rates
• surface area	• inequalities	• Pythagorean relationship

ISBN: 978-1-77149-206-5

⑦ The radius of a cone is twice the radius of a cylinder with the same height. What is the ratio of the volume of the cylinder to that of the cone? If the volume of the cone is 90 cm³, what is the volume of the cylinder?

⑧ Kenneth drew a square inside a circle as shown. The ratio of the square's side length to the circle's radius is $2:\sqrt{2}$. If the area of the square is 144 cm², what is the area of the circle?

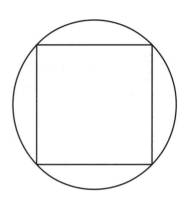

⑨ The coordinates of a point are (-3.5,-5.5). It is translated 5 units up and 2.5 units to the right. What are the coordinates of the new point? Daven joins the two points and says that the slope of the line must be positive. Is he correct? Explain.

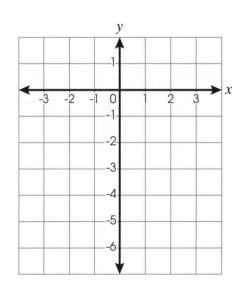

Topics covered:

Question 7	Question 8	Question 9
• ratios	• real numbers	• decimals
• volume	• ratios	• Cartesian coordinate plane
• polynomials	• circles	• graphs

ISBN: 978-1-77149-206-5

⑩ A prism has a base that is a quadrilateral with no right angles. The height of the prism is 15 cm and its volume is 720 cm³. What are 2 possible shapes of the prism's base and their dimensions?

⑪ Arnold painted a marble that had a radius of 3 cm. He used 0.156 mL of paint for 1 cm². How much paint did he use?

⑫ The ratio of red to blue marbles is 3:4 and the ratio of green to red marbles is 1:6. There is 1 green marble and one of the marbles is cracked. What is the probability that it is the green marble if it is certain that the marble is not red?

Topics covered:

Question 10	Question 11	Question 12
• volume	• proportions	• ratios
• angles	• surface area	• probability

ISBN: 978-1-77149-206-5

⑬ The distances in metres that the cyclists, Jon and Lynn, travel in t minutes are shown. Do they travel the same distance in t minutes? How far does Jon travel in $9\frac{1}{2}$ minutes?

Jon

$$d = t^2 + 9t$$

Lynn

$$d = \frac{8t^2(t + 3^2)}{2^3\sqrt{t^2}}$$

⑭ Together, Eddie, Roy, and Brian used more than 50 marbles for a school project. Brian used twice as many marbles as Eddie. Roy used $\frac{1}{4}$ as many marbles as Brian. What was the minimum number of marbles that Eddie used?

⑮ Leslie and Zack bike around a playground in the same direction. One lap is 210 m long. If Leslie bikes at 5 m/s and Zack bikes at 3.5 m/s, what time will they meet at the starting point if they start biking at 8:00 p.m.?

Topics covered:

Question 13	**Question 14**	**Question 15**
• fractions	• fractions	• decimals
• polynomials	• inequalities	• rates
• equations		

⑯ Thea hiked on a hill, from (-3,-4) to its image which is a $\frac{1}{2}$ rotation about (0,0). How far did she travel in metres? What is the slope of the hill?

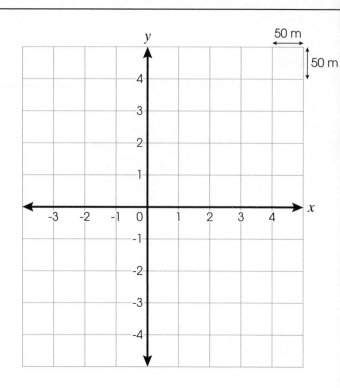

50 m

50 m

⑰ May has 28 candies in 4 different colours. Half of them are orange, blue, or green. The ratio of green to purple candies is 1:2. There is 1 fewer blue candy than green candy. If she picks 2 candies randomly without replacement, what is the probability that they are both blue candies?

Topics covered:

Question 16
- Pythagorean relationship
- Cartesian coordinate plane
- graphs

Question 17
- ratios
- probability

ISBN: 978-1-77149-206-5

Ann's house is 52 m east of Tim's and 48 m south of John's. If John goes to Tim's house through a straight path at a speed of 1.4 m/s, how long does it take John to get to Tim's house?

⑲ The price of a bag of chips increased from $1.99 to $2.50. The price of a bag of popcorn increased by the same percent. If a bag of popcorn is now $4.40, what was its original price?

⑳ Amanda and Joe left the library at 9:58. Amanda's house is 25 km away from the library and she arrived home at 10:35. Joe's house is 19 km away from the library and he arrived home at 10:28. Who had a higher speed?

Topics covered:

Question 18	**Question 19**	**Question 20**
• decimals	• decimals	• decimals
• rates	• percents	• rates
• Pythagorean relationship		

ISBN: 978-1-77149-206-5

Students are required to solve multi-step questions which involve various topics in each.

Topics Covered

	Number Sense and Numeration	Measurement	Geometry and Spatial Sense	Patterning and Algebra	Data Management and Probability	My Record ✔ correct ✗ incorrect
1	decimals percents					☐
2	fractions percents				probability	☐
3			Pythagorean relationship	equations		☐
4	percents	volume		polynomials		☐
5		circles	angles	inequalities		☐
6	fractions	volume	Pythagorean relationship			☐
7	real numbers				probability	☐
8		surface area		equations		☐
9			Cartesian coordinate plane	graphs		☐
10	decimals percents					☐
11		volume surface area	Pythagorean relationship			☐
12	ratios				probability	☐
13	fractions			inequalities		☐
14	proportions			equations		☐
15	rates	circles				☐
16			angles triangles	equations		☐
17	real numbers percents	circles				☐
18			Pythagorean relationship Cartesian coordinate plane	graphs		☐
19		volume surface area		equations		☐
20			angles triangles	equations		☐

ISBN: 978-1-77149-206-5

① A store is having a "buy one get one 50% off" promotion. David wants to buy 2 pairs of shoes that are $130.99 each. He has a 20%-off coupon but it cannot be combined with the store promotion. Which should he use to save more money, the coupon or the store promotion?

② 30% of a class are girls and $\frac{2}{3}$ of the class were born in Canada. If there are 30 students in the class and 6 girls were born in Canada, what is the probability that a randomly selected student will be a boy who was not born in Canada?

③ A bird's altitude in metres in t seconds is given as $a = 0.25t + 2.5$. If the bird travels for 10 s, what is its altitude? What is the value of x?

x m

altitude

6 m

Topics covered:

Question 1	**Question 2**	**Question 3**
• decimals	• fractions	• Pythagorean relationship
• percents	• percents	• equations
	• probability	

ISBN: 978-1-77149-206-5

④ If the radius of a cylinder is tripled, by how much will its volume increase in percent?

⑤ The distance of the arms of a compass and the angle that they make have the relationship shown. What is the area of the circle that the compass makes if its arms make an acute angle?

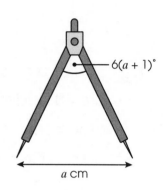

$6(a + 1)°$

a cm

⑥ A cube has a side length of 0.3 m. A triangular prism is cut out from it and its volume is $\frac{1}{25}$ of the cube's. If the base of the triangular prism is an isosceles triangle, what is its surface area?

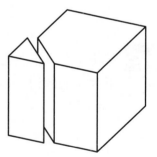

Topics covered:

Question 4	**Question 5**	**Question 6**
• percents	• circles	• fractions
• volume	• angles	• volume
• polynomials	• inequalities	• Pythagorean relationship

ISBN: 978-1-77149-206-5

Kylie has the cards shown.

$\dfrac{(-3)^4}{2}$	$-\sqrt{\dfrac{2^2}{7^0}}$	$(-2 + 3)^3$	$\left(\dfrac{3^7}{3^2}\right)^0$	$(-7) \times \left(\dfrac{1^{10}}{14}\right)$

Kylie has picked 2 cards without replacement. What is the probability that they are both less than -1?

 For an experiment, Michael tried to figure out how fast cubes move in a given space. He found that the speed at which a cube moves is related to its side length. The relation is $s = 7.1x + 9$ where s is speed in cm/s and x is the side length in cm. What is the speed of a cube that has a surface area of 54 cm^2?

Topics covered:

Question 7
- real numbers
- probability

Question 8
- surface area
- equations

ISBN: 978-1-77149-206-5

⑨ The coordinates of a point are (-1,3). It is rotated 180° about (1,0) and translated 1 unit up and 2 units to the left. Connect the 2 points. What is the slope of the line? Give the coordinates of a point on the line that is in Quadrant IV.

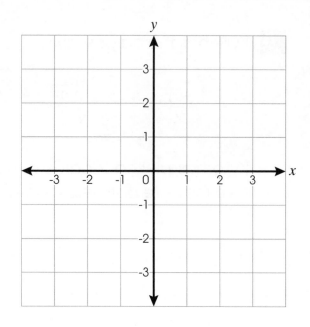

⑩ At a sale, all bouquets are sold at the same discount in percent. The price of a bouquet of roses is marked down from $29.20 to $20.44. If a bouquet of lilies was originally $19.25, how much does it cost after a 10% tax?

⑪ Hailey built a square-based pyramid as shown. Its surface area is 336 cm². What is its volume?

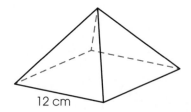

12 cm

Topics covered:

Question 9	**Question 10**	**Question 11**
• Cartesian coordinate plane	• decimals	• volume
• graphs	• percents	• surface area
		• Pythagorean relationship

ISBN: 978-1-77149-206-5

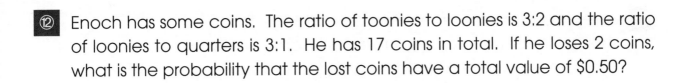

⑫ Enoch has some coins. The ratio of toonies to loonies is 3:2 and the ratio of loonies to quarters is 3:1. He has 17 coins in total. If he loses 2 coins, what is the probability that the lost coins have a total value of $0.50?

⑬ James measured the areas of his desk and his bedside table. The length of his desk triples its width. The length of the bedside table also triples its own width and its width is $\frac{1}{2}$ of the desk's width. If their difference in area is greater than 1 m², what is the area of the desk?

⑭ Mary threw a bowling pin. The height of the pin was related to the amount of time for which it had been in the air in seconds. She modelled it as $h = -t^2 + 4t + 2$ where h was height in metres and t was time in seconds. What were the heights of the bowling pin if it had been in the air for 2 s and 4 s? Was the time proportional to the height?

Topics covered:

Question 12	**Question 13**	**Question 14**
• ratios	• fractions	• proportions
• probability	• inequalities	• equations

⑮ Joseph and Adam are walking around the track shown. Joseph walks at 1.4 m/s and Adam walks 0.1 m/s faster. If they started walking in the same direction at the flag, after how long will they meet at the flag again?

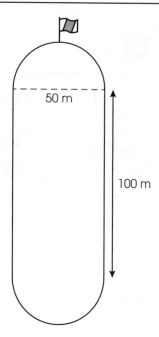

50 m

100 m

⑯ Zoe has drawn a shape that is made up of 2 triangles as shown. Are the triangles congruent?

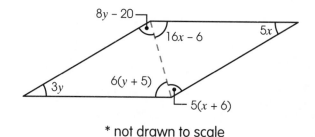

$8y - 20$

$16x - 6$

$5x$

$3y$

$6(y + 5)$

$5(x + 6)$

* not drawn to scale

⑰ Dina has drawn a clover that has a square and a semicircle on each of its sides. The area of the square is 196 cm². How much of the total area does the square take up in percent?

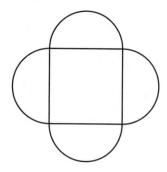

Topics covered:

Question 15
- rates
- circles

Question 16
- angles
- triangles
- equations

Question 17
- real numbers
- percents
- circles

ISBN: 978-1-77149-206-5

⑱ Sam dived into the water at (1,1) to a coordinate that is his original position's reflection in the x-axis and then translated 4 units to the left and 3 units down. What was the slope of his dive? What was the distance that Sam travelled?

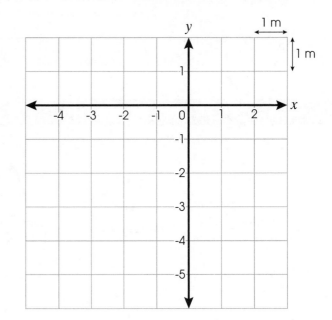

⑲ The height of a cylinder is 3 times its radius and its volume is 1177.5 cm³. What is its surface area?

⑳ 10th Street and 12th Avenue are parallel. Are Field ABC and Field DBC congruent?

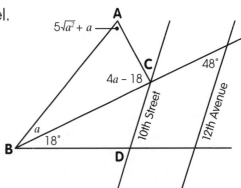

Topics covered:

Question 18
- Pythagorean relationship
- Cartesian coordinate plane
- graphs

Question 19
- volume
- surface area
- equations

Question 20
- angles
- triangles
- equations

ISBN: 978-1-77149-206-5

Students are required to solve multi-step questions which involve various topics in each.

Topics Covered

	Number Sense and Numeration	Measurement	Geometry and Spatial Sense	Patterning and Algebra	Data Management and Probability	My Record
1	real numbers		angles	equations		☐
2		circles volume				☐
3			Pythagorean relationship/triangles			☐
4	ratios	circles		inequalities		☐
5	fractions percents			inequalities		☐
6	rates		Pythagorean relationship			☐
7	ratios				probability	☐
8				graphs equations		☐
9	percents	volume				☐
10		volume		polynomials		☐
11	percents	surface area				☐
12			Pythagorean relationship	equations		☐
13	ratios				probability	☐
14			Pythagorean relationship/angles			☐
15		volume surface area		equations		☐
16	fractions				data management	☐
17				inequalities	data management	☐
18	rates	volume				☐
19			Cartesian coordinate plane	graphs		☐
20				polynomials graphs/relations		☐

My Record: ✔ correct ✗ incorrect

ISBN: 978-1-77149-206-5

① Mareen thinks that she cannot find the perimeter of the triangle shown. Is she correct? If not, what is the perimeter?

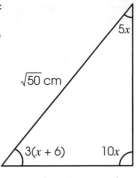

5x

√50 cm

3(x + 6)   10x

* not drawn to scale

② One rotation of the paint roller shown covers an area of 376.8 cm². What is the volume of the roller?

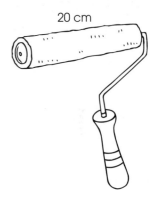

20 cm

③ The shaded triangles are congruent. What is the perimeter of △ABC?

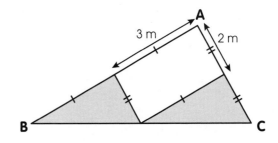

A

3 m   2 m

B   C

Topics covered:

Question 1	Question 2	Question 3
• real numbers	• circles	• Pythagorean relationship
• angles	• volume	• triangles
• equations		

ISBN: 978-1-77149-206-5

④ The ratio of the radius of a small pizza to that of a large pizza is 2:3. If the area of the small pizza is greater than 452.16 cm², what is the circumference of the large pizza?

⑤ Tim bought a used car for $3600 and paid $1400 to repair it. He then sold it and made a profit of more than 55%. He spent $\frac{4}{5}$ of the profit on the down payment of his new car. How much was the down payment?

⑥ A grasshopper travels at 0.97 m/leap. If it wants to get to the top of the hill, how many leaps will it have to make?

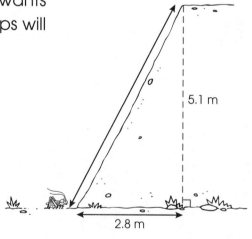

5.1 m

2.8 m

Topics covered:

Question 4	**Question 5**	**Question 6**
• ratios	• fractions	• rates
• circles	• percents	• Pythagorean relationship
• inequalities	• inequalities	

ISBN: 978-1-77149-206-5

⑦ Terry has 29 tokens for a board game. The ratio of cars to houses is 4:3 and it is 2:5 for houses to coins. If his 2 friends pick their own tokens, what is the probability that they both pick houses?

⑧ The coordinates of a point are (4,-3). Elsa translated it 6 units to the left and some units up. She drew a line to connect the points and the slope of the line is $-\frac{2}{3}$. What is the y-coordinate of the translated point?

⑨ A cone is inside a box as shown. What is the volume of the cone? How much of the box's volume does the cone take up in percent?

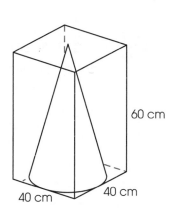

60 cm

40 cm   40 cm

Topics covered:

Question 7	Question 8	Question 9
• ratios	• graphs	• percents
• probability	• equations	• volume

⑩ The thickness of a roll of toilet paper is the same as the diameter of the roll in the centre. What is the volume of the toilet paper in regard to x if the volume of the hollow space in the centre is $8.635x^2$?

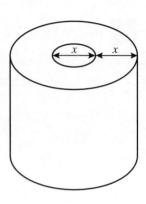

⑪ The height of a box is 3 cm more than its length. Its width is 50% of its height. What is the surface area if the length of the box is 5 cm?

⑫ A right isosceles triangle has an area of 33.62 cm². What are its height and hypotenuse?

Topics covered:

Question 10	**Question 11**	**Question 12**
• volume	• percents	• Pythagorean relationship
• polynomials	• surface area	• equations

ISBN: 978-1-77149-206-5

⑬ Vienna's drawer has 4 white socks and the ratio of white to black socks is 2:1. There is also 1 green sock. What is the probability that Vienna will pick a pair of colour-matching socks?

⑭ A see-saw has a pivot that is an equilateral triangle as shown. What angle does the resting board make with the ground? If the distance from the centre of the base of the pivot to one end of the board is 150 cm, what is the length of the entire board?

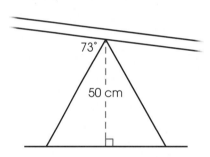

⑮ Louise is blowing bubbles. If the volume of the bubble is 36π cm³, what is its surface area?

Topics covered:

Question 13	**Question 14**	**Question 15**
• ratios	• Pythagorean relationship	• volume
• probability	• angles	• surface area
		• equations

ISBN: 978-1-77149-206-5

⑯ A condominium's management created a circle graph of the age groups of its residents. There are 96 residents who are from 41 to 60 years old. How many residents are there from 0 to 40 years old?

Age Groups of Residents

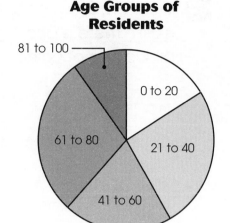

⑰ Refer to Question 16. For the residents who are from 0 to 40 years old, twice as many attend school as those who work. More than 35 of them neither attend school nor go to work. How many residents from 0 to 40 years old go to work?

⑱ The amount of water that flows from a faucet is 205 mL/s. A pail has the dimensions shown. How long does it take to fill up the pail?

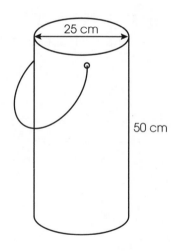

25 cm

50 cm

Topics covered:

Question 16	Question 17	Question 18
• fractions	• inequalities	• rates
• data management	• data management	• volume

ISBN: 978-1-77149-206-5

⑲ Point M is at (-2,5) and Point N is the reflection of Point M in the y-axis. Connect the points. What is the slope of the line?

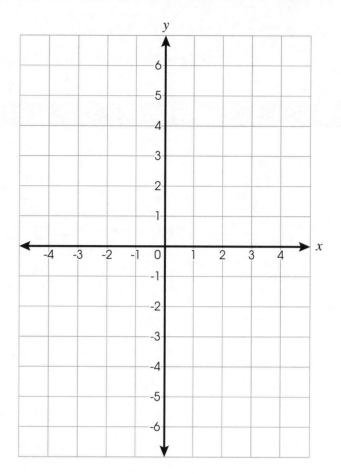

⑳ Refer to Question 19. Trisha thinks that the two relations, $y = 2x + 3$ and $y = \dfrac{\sqrt{4x^3}}{x^2} + \dfrac{3\sqrt{b^2}}{b}$, are the same. Is she correct? If so, graph the relation. At which point does the relation intersect $\overline{MN}$?

Topics covered:

Question 19
- Cartesian coordinate plane
- graphs

Question 20
- polynomials
- graphs
- relations

ISBN: 978-1-77149-206-5

Critical-thinking Questions – Level 2

Students are required to solve multi-step questions which involve various topics in each.

Topics Covered

	Number Sense and Numeration	Measurement	Geometry and Spatial Sense	Patterning and Algebra	Data Management and Probability	My Record ✔ correct ✗ incorrect
1	fractions				probability	
2	percents decimals			equations		
3		circles	Pythagorean relationship	equations		
4	percents	volume				
5		surface area	Pythagorean relationship			
6			Pythagorean relationship	graphs		
7			Pythagorean relationship/angles			
8	decimals			inequalities	data management	
9	ratios	volume				
10			Pythagorean relationship Cartesian coordinate plane			
11			Cartesian coordinate plane	graphs		
12	percents	volume		inequalities		
13		surface area		polynomials inequalities		
14	fractions rates		Pythagorean relationship			
15	rates	circles				
16	fractions ratios					
17				equations inequalities		
18			angles triangles			
19	percents proportions				probability	
20	ratios		triangles			

① In a pile of 56 number cards, $\frac{3}{8}$ of them are negative, $\frac{4}{7}$ are positive, and the rest are "0". Peter picks 2 cards without replacement and multiplies them. What is the probability that the product is positive if one of the cards is negative?

② Juliet bought a used watch. She increased the price by 75% and then sold it to Romeo with a 12% tax. Including a shipping fee of $4.96, Romeo paid a total of $63.76. How much did Juliet buy the watch for?

③ A rug has the design shown. The area of the right isosceles triangle is 2.5 m². What is the area of the rug?

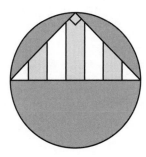

Topics covered:

Question 1
- fractions
- probability

Question 2
- percents
- decimals
- equations

Question 3
- Pythagorean relationship
- circles
- equations

ISBN: 978-1-77149-206-5

④ The container with the dimensions shown is filled with water. The water will be poured into a cylindrical container with a radius of 20 cm and a height of 20 cm. How much of the cylinder will be filled in percent?

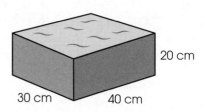

20 cm

30 cm   40 cm

⑤ Denise wants to paint a cube that has a diagonal of 14 cm on each face. What is the surface area of the cube?

⑥ The relations of 3 lines are given below.

$$y = x$$
$$y = -x - 2$$
$$y = x - 6$$

Graph the lines. Are there any intersections? If so, mark them as M and N and connect them. What is the length of $\overline{MN}$?

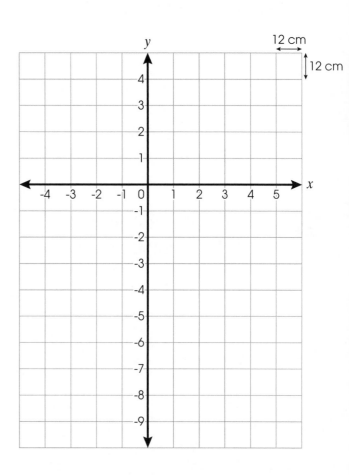

12 cm

12 cm

Topics covered:

Question 4	**Question 5**	**Question 6**
• percents	• Pythagorean relationship	• Pythagorean relationship
• volume	• surface area	• graphs

ISBN: 978-1-77149-206-5

⑦ Toby has twisted a piece of wire into 2 triangles as shown. What are the angles of the big triangle? What is the length of the piece of wire?

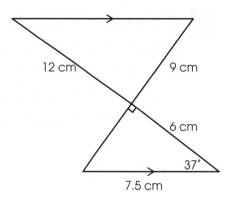

⑧ Freddie's first 8 tests had a mean score of 83.5% and there was no mode. After 2 more tests, his mean was greater than 85% and the mode was 86%. What scores did he get on the last 2 tests?

⑨ 3 cylinders are inside a box as shown. The ratio of their heights is 2:5:3. How much greater is the volume of the biggest cylinder than the smallest one?

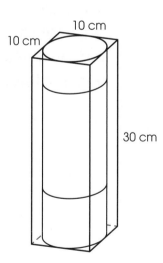

Topics covered:

Question 7	**Question 8**	**Question 9**
• Pythagorean relationship	• decimals	• ratios
• angles	• inequalities	• volume
	• data management	

ISBN: 978-1-77149-206-5

⑩ Cecilia has plotted the 2 points shown. She plots 2 other points that are the 180° rotations of the first 2 points about (0,0) to form a quadrilateral. Name the quadrilateral and find its perimeter.

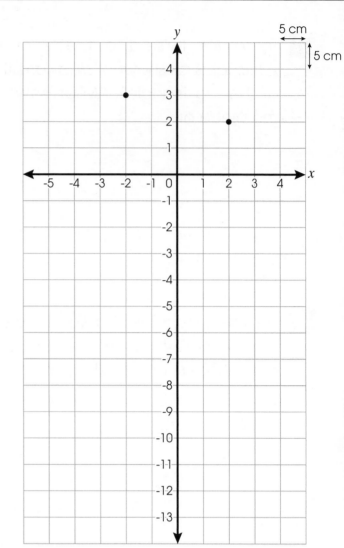

⑪ Refer to Question 10. Cecilia draws a line of reflection. One end point of the line is (3,-5) and the other end point is its translation of 7 units to the left. What is the slope of the line of reflection? Reflect the quadrilateral in the line.

Topics covered:

Question 10
- Pythagorean relationship
- Cartesian coordinate plane

Question 11
- Cartesian coordinate plane
- graphs

ISBN: 978-1-77149-206-5

⑫ Alice wants to design a container. It will be a rectangular prism with a minimum capacity of 24 L. If she wants the width to be half of the height and the length to be 150% of the width, what will be the minimum height of the container?

⑬ To find the surface area of a sphere, Beatrice uses the formula: $\dfrac{\sqrt{64\pi^2 r^4}}{2}$. Will it yield the correct answer? If the surface area is at least 113.04 cm², what is its radius?

⑭ Joseph and Benjamin left the airport. Joseph travelled east at a speed of 878 km/h and Benjamin travelled north at 726 km/h. They arrived at their destinations after $1\frac{1}{2}$ h and 2 h respectively. How far apart were their destinations?

Topics covered:

Question 12	Question 13	Question 14
• percents	• surface area	• fractions
• volume	• polynomials	• rates
• inequalities	• inequalities	• Pythagorean relationship

Wendy and Derek are racing on a track that is in the shape of a circle with a diameter of 20 m. Wendy runs at a speed of 4 m/s and Derek runs at 3.2 m/s. How long will it take Wendy to outrun Derek by 1 lap?

⑯ Geoff has a bag of nickels, dimes, and quarters. The number of dimes is $\frac{3}{4}$ of the quarters. The ratio of nickels to dimes is 5:8. How much does Geoff have in total if he has $16 in quarters?

⑰ The profit a company makes is modelled by $p = 0.8n^2 + 0.5n - 14.8$ where p is profit and n is the number of items sold. How much will they make after selling 2 items and then 20 items? They want to find out at least how many items must they sell to make a profit. Help them set up an inequality.

Topics covered:

Question 15	Question 16	Question 17
• rates	• fractions	• equations
• circles	• ratios	• inequalities

ISBN: 978-1-77149-206-5

⑱ Scarlet used sticks to create the design shown. Is there a pair of congruent triangles that have right angles? If so, how do you know that they are congruent?

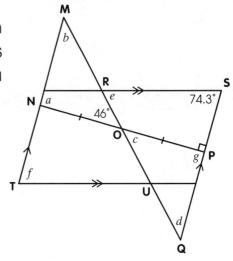

⑲ 50 marbles weigh 1.5 kg and the number of marbles is proportional to their total weight. The total weight of a basket of marbles is 6 kg. $\frac{1}{4}$ of them are green, 31% are red, and the rest are blue. Joe picks 2 marbles without replacement. What is the probability that the second marble is green if the first one is blue?

⑳ The lengths of 3 sides of a triangle have a ratio of 1:3:2 and the perimeter of the triangle is 15 cm. What are the lengths? The lengths of the sides of another triangle also have the ratio of 1:3:2. Maverick thinks that the triangles must be congruent. Is he correct? Explain.

Topics covered:

Question 18
- angles
- triangles

Question 19
- percents
- proportions
- probability

Question 20
- ratios
- triangles

ISBN: 978-1-77149-206-5

Students are required to solve multi-step questions which involve various topics in each.

Topics Covered

	Number Sense and Numeration	Measurement	Geometry and Spatial Sense	Patterning and Algebra	Data Management and Probability	My Record ✔ correct ✘ incorrect
1	fractions rates	volume				☐
2	decimals percents					☐
3			Pythagorean relationship/angles			☐
4	rates	surface area				☐
5	decimals percents					☐
6		volume		equations		☐
7	ratios				probability	☐
8	rates			inequalities		☐
9	real numbers				probability	☐
10				graphs relations		☐
11	real numbers percents					☐
12			Pythagorean relationship/angles			☐
13			angles triangles			☐
14		circles	Pythagorean relationship			☐
15	ratios		angles			☐
16	fractions decimals/percents					☐
17	fractions			equations	data management	☐
18		volume surface area		inequalities		☐
19				polynomials	probability	☐
20			Pythagorean relationship Cartesian coordinate plane			☐

ISBN: 978-1-77149-206-5

① A cylindrical tank has a radius of 10 cm. Water is pumped into it at the rate of 10 mL/s. What is the water level of the tank after $1\frac{2}{5}$ min?

② A $3.99-bag of candies is on sale for "buy 3 get 1 free" in-store or 20% off online. Mary wants 16 bags of candies. If there is a $5 shipping fee for online purchases, should Mary buy the candies in-store or online?

③ A desktop is shown. What is the measure of Angle a? What is the perimeter of the desktop?

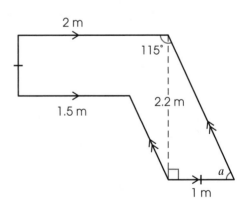

Topics covered:

Question 1	**Question 2**	**Question 3**
• fractions	• decimals	• Pythagorean relationship
• rates	• percents	• angles
• volume		

④ Ellen wants to build a square-based pyramid with plywood. The pyramid will have a height of 82 cm and the area of its base will be 625 cm². How much will the plywood cost if it is $8.55/m²?

⑤ In the first 6 tests, Robert got a mean of 18.5 correct answers. After 4 more tests, the mean number of correct answers was 20.1. By how much had his mean improved in percent?

⑥ Donna made a sphere with modelling clay. She then reshaped it into a cylinder. The radii of the sphere and the cylinder were both 2 cm. What was the height of the cylinder?

Topics covered:

Question 4	Question 5	Question 6
• rates	• decimals	• volume
• surface area	• percents	• equations

ISBN: 978-1-77149-206-5

⑦ Angelica's piggy bank has dimes, quarters, and loonies. The ratio of golden coins to silver coins is 1:9 and the ratio of loonies to quarters is 2:3. There is a total of $12.75. If Angelica loses 2 coins, what is the probability that they are both silver coins?

⑧ Gary swam at a speed of 2.5 m/s with front crawl and completed a lap in 32 s. With backstroke, he needed more than $\frac{2}{3}$ min to complete the lap. What was his speed with backstroke?

⑨ There are 2 rounds in a game. In each round, a player picks a ball with replacement and spins the wheel. The ball determines the sign of the number spun. The numbers from both rounds are added. What is the probability that a player gets a sum of +8?

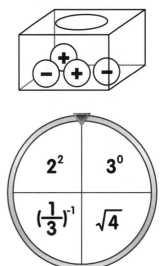

Topics covered:

Question 7	Question 8	Question 9
• ratios	• rates	• real numbers
• probability	• inequalities	• probability

⑩ The graph shows the relationship between Celsius and Fahrenheit, where c is the temperature in degrees Celsius and f is degrees in Fahrenheit. Which relation below describes the relationship?

(A) $f = \dfrac{9}{5} c + 32$

(B) $f = c + 36$

A cup of water was 77°F. What was its temperature in degrees Celsius?

 ⑪ Refer to Question 10. Laura added ice to the cup of water so that the water is now half of the square root of the initial temperature in degrees Celsius. How much has the temperature dropped in percent?

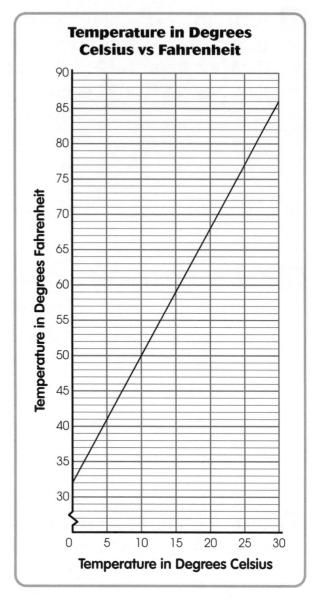

Temperature in Degrees Celsius vs Fahrenheit

Temperature in Degrees Fahrenheit

Temperature in Degrees Celsius

Topics covered:

Question 10
• graphs
• relations

Question 11
• real numbers
• percents

ISBN: 978-1-77149-206-5

⑫ The trapezoid shown is made up of an isosceles triangle and a right triangle. What are the sizes of the angles in both triangles? If the area of the isosceles triangle is 25.9 cm², what is its perimeter?

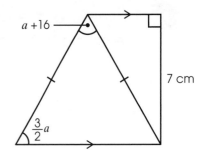

⑬ One of the angles in a rhombus measures 56°. Justin has cut it into 2 triangles and he says, "These two triangles are congruent." Is he correct? If so, what are the measures of the angles in each triangle?

⑭ Frank placed 4 identical coasters inside a square frame as shown. The diagonal of the frame is 19.8 cm. What is the area of each coaster?

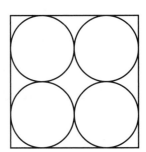

Topics covered:

Question 12
- Pythagorean relationship
- angles

Question 13
- angles
- triangles

Question 14
- circles
- Pythagorean relationship

ISBN: 978-1-77149-206-5

⑮ The ratio of the angles in a quadrilateral is 1:2:2:3. What are the sizes of the angles? Name the quadrilateral.

⑯ Over 7 days, Ken has drunk a mean of 0.175 L of juice each day and his sister has drunk a mean of $\frac{1}{5}$ L. How much juice was in the carton initially if 12.5% of it is left?

⑰ Mavis did a survey on the devices the students at her school own. If 320 students were surveyed, how many of them own phones? For those who own phones, the number of students who have data plans is $\frac{1}{5}$ of those who do not. How many students who own phones do not have data plans?

Devices Students Own

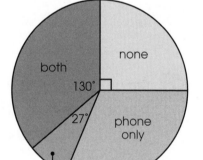

tablet only

Topics covered:

Question 15	**Question 16**	**Question 17**
• ratios	• fractions	• fractions
• angles	• decimals	• equations
	• percents	• data management

ISBN: 978-1-77149-206-5

⑱ Roy has designed a can that has a capacity of less than 602.9 mL. Its height is 50% greater than its diameter. What is the maximum radius of the can? What is its maximum surface area?

⑲ Rachel picks 2 cards without replacement. She will win the game if the values of the cards are equal. What is the probability that she will win?

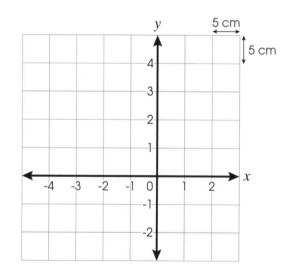

$$\sqrt{x^2 y^2} \qquad (xy)^{-1}$$

$$\frac{2xy}{\sqrt{4}} \qquad \frac{x^3 yz}{x^2}$$

$$(xyz)^{\circ} \qquad x + y$$

⑳ The vertices of a triangle are at (1,3), (1,0), and (-3,-1). Its image is a rotation of 180° about (-1,1). The two triangles combine to form a shape. What is the perimeter of the shape?

Topics covered:

Question 18
- volume
- surface area
- inequalities

Question 19
- polynomials
- probability

Question 20
- Pythagorean relationship
- Cartesian coordinate plane

ISBN: 978-1-77149-206-5

ISBN: 978-1-77149-206-5

Answers

Basic Problem-solving Questions

1 Real Numbers

Math Skills

1. 2
2. 4
3. 6
4. -3
5. -8
6. 6
7. 3^{2+4} ; 3^6 ; 729
8. 4^{3+2} ; 4^5 ; 1024
9. 6^{3-2} ; 6^1 ; 6
10. 2^{10-10} ; 2^0 ; 1
11. 3 ; 2 ; 6
12. $\frac{\sqrt{4}}{\sqrt{9}}$; $\frac{2}{3}$
13. $\sqrt{16} \times \sqrt{25}$; 4×5 ; 20
14. $\frac{\sqrt{16}}{\sqrt{25}}$; $\frac{4}{5}$
15. $= 2^{8-6} + 3^{1+2}$
 $= 2^2 + 3^3$
 $= 4 + 27$
 $= 31$
16. $= 5^2 \div (3 + 2)$
 $= 5^2 \div 5$
 $= 5^{2-1}$
 $= 5$
17. $= \sqrt{9^{-1} \times 9}$
 $= \sqrt{9^{-1+1}}$
 $= \sqrt{9^0}$
 $= \sqrt{1}$
 $= 1$
18. $= \frac{2^4}{2^3} \times \frac{3^7}{3^8} \times \frac{5^3}{5^4}$
 $= 2 \times \frac{1}{3} \times \frac{1}{5}$
 $= \frac{2}{15}$
19. $= 6^3 \div 6^2$
 $= 6^{3-2}$
 $= 6$
20. $= \frac{4 - 9 + 1}{16 \div (-8)}$
 $= \frac{-4}{-2}$
 $= 2$

Problem Solving

-20 ; -18 ; 18 ; -20 ; -20

1a. $(-10) \times 2 + 4 \times 2 = -20 + 8 = -12$; -12

b. Jordan's mean score: $(-20) \div 4 = -5$
Sam's mean score: $(-12) \div 4 = -3$
Difference: $(-3) - (-5) = 2$
Sam ; 2

2a. $((-8) + (-3) + 0 + (-2) + 8) \div 5 = (-5) \div 5 = -1$
-1

b. $(-1) \times 2 - 5 = (-2) - 5 = -7$
-7

3a. Greatest product: $(-6) \times (-8) = 48$
Least product: $2 \times (-8) = -16$
Difference: $48 - (-16) = 64$
64

b. The change is from 2 to -2. The product of 2 negative numbers is always positive.

4. $5^2 \times 5^3 = 5^{2+3} = 5^5 = 3125$; 3125

5. $4^7 \div 4^5 = 4^{7-5} = 4^2 = 16$; 16

6a. $3^4 \times 3^5 = 3^{4+5} = 3^9 = 19\,683$; 19 683

b. $3^9 \times 3 = 3^{9+1} = 3^{10}$; 3^{10}

7. $2^{23} \div 2^{15} = 2^{23-15} = 2^8 = 256$
It is 256 times larger.

8. $10^7 \div 100 = 10^7 \div 10^2 = 10^{7-2} = 10^5 = 100\,000$
100 000 $100 bills are needed.

9a. $3^4 \div 3^3 = 3^{4-3} = 3$
Brian can build 3 of Frame 3.

b. $3^3 \times 3 \div 3^2 = 3^{3+1-2} = 3^2 = 9$
Brian can build 9 of Frame 2.

10a. $\sqrt{4^2 + 3^2} = \sqrt{16 + 9} = \sqrt{25} = 5$
The side length will be 5 m.

b. $5^2 \div (0.2)^2 = 25 \div 0.04 = 625$
There are 625 tiles.

11. $\sqrt{12} \times \sqrt{3} = \sqrt{12 \times 3} = \sqrt{36} = 6$
The area of the garage is 6 m².

12. $\frac{\sqrt{400}}{\sqrt{100}} = \sqrt{\frac{400}{100}} = \sqrt{4} = 2$
It is 2 times larger.

13. $10^4 \div 10^{-1} = 10^{4-(-1)} = 10^{4+1} = 10^5 = 100\,000$
It can be 100 000 times bigger than its seed.

14. $5^{-3} \times 5^8 = 5^{(-3)+8} = 5^5$
A honeybee can travel 5^5 m.

15. $2.5 \times 10^{-11} \times 1.64 \times 10^{15}$
$= 2.5 \times 1.64 \times 10^{(-11)+15}$
$= 4.1 \times 10^4$
There are 4.1×10^4 plankton.

16a. $1.5 \times 10^7 \div 12 = 0.125 \times 10^7 = 1.25 \times 10^6$
The mean number of visitors in a month was 1.25×10^6.

b. $\$1.16 \times 10^3 \times 1.5 \times 10^7 = \$1.74 \times 10^{10}$
The tourists contributed $\$1.74 \times 10^{10}$.

17. Area of square park: $11^2 \times 11^2 = 11^4$
$11^4 \div 11^3 = 11$
The square park has a greater area by 11 times.

18a. $(-3)^2 = (-3) \times (-3) = 9$
$-3^2 = -(3 \times 3) = -9$
Kyle is incorrect.

b. $(\sqrt{25})^2 = 5^2 = 25$
William is correct.

c. $6^2 = 36$
$(-6)^2 = (-6) \times (-6) = 36$
Sandra is correct.

d. $\sqrt{9^2} = \sqrt{81} = 9$
Alfred is correct.

2 Fractions and Decimals

Math Skills

1. $\frac{3}{28}$
2. $\frac{5}{6}$
3. $\frac{7}{20}$
4. $2\frac{1}{8}$
5. $4\frac{1}{2}$
6. $6\frac{5}{6}$
7. $\frac{1}{6}$
8. 43.75
9. 63
10. 0.12
11. 0.145
12. 0.235
13. 35.8
14. 1.365
15. 6.1
16. 11.74

ISBN: 978-1-77149-206-5

0.25 ; $\frac{2}{5}$; 0.375 ; $1\frac{1}{5}$; 1.75 ; $3\frac{1}{2}$; 2.8

17. 0.25 ; 1.1 18. $\frac{3}{5} \div (\frac{1}{2} + \frac{2}{5})$; $\frac{2}{3}$

19. $1.8 \div 0.375 - 1.03$; 3.77

20. $1\frac{1}{5} + 1\frac{5}{6} \times 2\frac{1}{4} = 5\frac{13}{40}$

21. $10.2 - 1.75 \times 2.1$; 6.525

22. $2\frac{1}{2} \times \frac{6}{7} + 3\frac{1}{2} \times 1\frac{1}{7}$; $6\frac{1}{7}$

23. $2.8 \div 0.4 - 2.6 \div 1.3$; 5

Problem Solving

$3\frac{1}{3}$; $\frac{20}{3}$; $\frac{3}{2}$; 10 ; $3\frac{1}{3}$; $3\frac{1}{3}$

1. $6\frac{2}{3} - 6\frac{2}{3} \times \frac{3}{4} = 6\frac{2}{3} - \frac{20}{3} \times \frac{3}{4} = 6\frac{2}{3} - 5 = 1\frac{2}{3}$

$1\frac{2}{3}$

2. $4\frac{4}{5} \div 2\frac{1}{4} \times 10$ 3. $1 - \frac{1}{10} - \frac{1}{8} \times 6$

$= \frac{24}{5} \times \frac{4}{9} \times \frac{10}{1}$ $= 1 - \frac{1}{10} - \frac{3}{4}$

$= 21\frac{1}{3}$ $= \frac{3}{20}$

$21\frac{1}{3}$ $\frac{3}{20}$

4. $2 - \frac{3}{5} - \frac{2}{3} \times 2$ 5. $3\frac{1}{3} \div (1 - \frac{1}{6}) \times \frac{1}{6}$

$= 2 - \frac{3}{5} - \frac{4}{3}$ $= \frac{10}{3} \div \frac{5}{6} \times \frac{1}{6}$

$= \frac{1}{15}$ $= \frac{2}{3}$

$\frac{1}{15}$ $\frac{2}{3}$

6. $20 \times \frac{2}{5} - 20 \times \frac{3}{10} = 8 - 6 = 2$; 2

7. $\frac{4}{5} \times 1\frac{1}{2} \times (1 - \frac{1}{6}) = \frac{4}{5} \times \frac{3}{2} \times \frac{5}{6} = 1$; 1

8a. $8\frac{1}{2} \times (1 - \frac{1}{10}) \div \frac{17}{20} = \frac{17}{2} \times \frac{9}{10} \times \frac{20}{17} = 9$; 9

b. $8\frac{1}{2} \times \frac{1}{10} + \frac{17}{20} \times 4$

$= \frac{17}{2} \times \frac{1}{10} + \frac{17}{20} \times \frac{4}{1}$

$= \frac{17}{20} + \frac{68}{20} = 4\frac{1}{4}$

$4\frac{1}{4}$

9. $\$0.99 \times 12 - \$10.99 = \$11.88 - \$10.99 = \$0.89$
It costs $0.89 more.

10. $60 - 60 \times 0.95 = 60 - 57 = 3$
3 test results are inaccurate.

11. $4.2 \div (0.25 + 0.1) = 4.2 \div 0.35 = 12$
It will take Justin 12 days.

12. $(\$17.60 - \$12.35) \times 2.8 = \$5.25 \times 2.8 = \$14.70$
Mr. Sun saved $14.70.

13. $(2.68 - 2.68 \times 0.1) \div 4 = 2.412 \div 4 = 0.603$
There were 0.603 kg of snacks in each bag.

14. $5.5 \times 4 + (5.5 + 1.25) = 22 + 6.75 = 28.75$
The total length of the ribbon is 28.75 m.

15a. $(\$5.25 + \$2.19) \div (0.75 + 0.45) = \$7.44 \div 1.2 = \$6.20$
1 L of shampoo in value size costs $6.20.

b. $\$5.25 \div 0.75 \times 6 - \$6.20 \times 6 = \$4.80$
She will save $4.80.

16. $\$51.78 \div \frac{3}{4} = \$51.78 \div 0.75 = \$69.04$

It would have cost $69.04.

17. Cheese: $\$5.50 \div \frac{2}{3} = \$5.50 \times \frac{3}{2} = \$8.25$

Pepperoni: $\$4.55 \div \frac{5}{8} = \$4.55 \div 0.625 = \$7.28$
The pepperoni pizza is a better deal.

18. $\$6.33 \times \frac{1}{2} \times \frac{1}{4} = \$0.79$

$\frac{1}{4}$ kg of beans will cost $0.79.

19. $\$0.25 \times 3 \div \frac{1}{4} \times 1\frac{1}{2} = \$4.50$

It would have cost $4.50.

20. $2.64 \times \frac{7}{8} + 1.32 \times \frac{3}{5} = 2.31 + 0.792 = 3.102$

Jason made 3.102 L of fruit punch.

21. $(1.15 + 2\frac{4}{5}) \div 1\frac{2}{3} = 3.95 \times \frac{3}{5} = 2.37$

There is 2.37 kg of concrete in 1 hole.

22. $0.84 \div 1\frac{2}{5} \times 2\frac{4}{5} = 0.84 \div 1.4 \times 2.8 = 1.68$

Dino should make 1.68 L of tomato sauce.

23. $\$50 - (\$12.75 \div \frac{1}{3} - \$12.75) = \$50 - \$25.50 = \$24.50$

Connie's change was $24.50.

24. $0.4 \times (8.25 \div \frac{1}{5} - 2.5) = 0.4 \times 38.75 = 15.5$

The mass of the remaining rope is 15.5 kg.

25. $(\$2.40 \times 3) \div (\$2.40 \times \frac{3}{4}) = \$7.20 \div \$1.80 = 4$

4 apples can be bought.

3   Percents

Math Skills

1. 0.5 ; 10 2. 60×0.1 ; 6
3. 28×0.07 ; 1.96 4. 250×0.18 ; 45
5. 32×0.165 ; 5.28 6. 8×0.002 ; 0.016
7. $200 \times 15\%$ 8. $32 \times 8\%$
$= 200 \times 0.15$ $= 32 \times 0.08$
$= 30$ $= 2.56$
9. $0.85 \times 34\%$ 10. $4 \times 125\%$
$= 0.85 \times 0.34$ $= 4 \times 1.25$
$= 0.289$ $= 5$
11. $400 \times 14.25\%$ 12. $32 \times 8.15\%$
$= 400 \times 0.1425$ $= 32 \times 0.0815$
$= 57$ $= 2.608$
13a. $\frac{4}{10} \times 100\%$ b. $\frac{110 - 80}{80} \times 100\%$

40% $= \frac{30}{80} \times 100\%$

                              $= 37.5\%$

ISBN: 978-1-77149-206-5

c. $\dfrac{24.03 - 21.36}{21.36} \times 100\%$

$= \dfrac{2.67}{21.36} \times 100\%$

$= 12.5\%$

d. $\dfrac{16.75 - 10.72}{16.75} \times 100\%$

$= \dfrac{6.03}{16.75} \times 100\%$

$= 36\%$

Problem Solving

60 ; 60

1a. $\$1300 \times 5\% \times 3 = \$195$; 195

b. $\$1300 \times 5\% \times \dfrac{1}{4} = \$16.25$; 16.25

2a. $\$2200 \times 4.5\% \times \dfrac{3}{4} = \$74.25$; 74.25

b. $\$2200 + \$2200 \times 4.5\% \times 6 = \$2794$; 2794

3a. $\$3500 \times 3.6\% \times 2\dfrac{1}{2} = \$315$; 315

b. $\$3500 + \$3500 \times 3.6\% \times 5 = \$4130$; 4130

4. $\$1500 \times 2\% \times (3 \div \dfrac{1}{2}) = \$1500 \times 2\% \times 6 = \$180$
180

5. $96 = 1200 \times i \times 4$
$i = 0.02$
2%

6. Interest: $\$834 - \$695 = \$139$
$139 = 695 \times 5\% \times t$
$t = 4$
4

7. Doubling the investment means that the interest earned will be $350.
$350 = 350 \times 12.5\% \times t$
$t = 8$
8

8a. $\$135 \times (1 + 14\%) = \$135 \times 114\% = \$153.90$
The jacket will cost $153.90.

b. $\$68 \times (1 + 14\%) - \$42.99 \times (1 + 14\%)$
$= \$68 \times 114\% - \$42.99 \times 114\%$
$= \$28.51$
The sweater will cost $28.51 more.

c. $\$89.50 \times (1 + 14\%) - \$89.50 \times (1 - 15\%) \times (1 + 14\%)$
$= \$89.50 \times 114\% - \$89.50 \times 85\% \times 114\%$
$= 15.30$
$15.30 will be saved.

d. $(\$25.75 + \$68 + \$135 + \$42.99 + \$89.50) \times (1 - 15\%) \times (1 + 14\%)$
$= \$361.24 \times 85\% \times 114\%$
$= \$350.04$
No, $345 is not enough.

9a. $\$1080 \times 30\% \times 20 = \$6480$
Best Electronics will make $6480 in profit.

b. $\$1080 \times (1 + 30\%) \times 3.5\% \times 5$
$= \$1080 \times 130\% \times 3.5\% \times 5$
$= \$245.70$
John will earn $245.70 in commission.

10. $\$200 \times (1 - 20\%) \times (1 - 15\%) \times (1 + 13\%)$
$= \$200 \times 80\% \times 85\% \times 113\%$
$= \$153.68$
Marsha will pay $153.68 for the dress.

11. $\$45.50 \times (1 + 13\%) - \$45.50 \times (1 + 5\%)$
$= \$45.50 \times 113\% - \$45.50 \times 105\%$
$= \$3.64$
The difference is $3.64.

12. $\$1590.40 \div (1 + 12\%) \div (1 - 75\%)$
$= \$1590.40 \div 112\% \div 25\%$
$= \$5680$
The couch's original price was $5680.

13. $\dfrac{\$290 - \$216.05}{\$290} \times 100\% = 25.5\%$
The discount rate is 25.5%.

14. $\dfrac{16.5 - 15}{15} \times 100\% = 10\%$
The temperature increased by 10%.

15. $\dfrac{\$12.60 - \$11.20}{\$11.20} \times 100\% = 12.5\%$
The raise was 12.5%.

16. $\dfrac{8.294 - 7.54}{7.54} \times 100\% = 10\%$
He has gained 10% in weight.

17. $1250 \times 8\% \times 3 + (\$3000 - \$1250) \times 5\% \times 2$
$= \$300 + \$175$
$= \$475$
Shane will earn $475 in interest.

18. $\$45\,282 \times 15\% + (\$60\,000 - \$45\,282) \times 20.5\%$
$= \$6792.30 + \$3017.19$
$= \$9809.49$
Carly paid $9809.49 in federal tax.

19a. $\$24.54 \div 1.5\% = \$1636$
The price of the fridge was $1636.

b. $\dfrac{\$1766.88 - \$1636}{\$1636} \times 100\% = 8\%$
The tax rate was 8%.

c. Commission: $\$1636 \times (1 - 15\%) \times 1.5\% = \$20.86$
Cost: $\$1636 \times (1 - 15\%) \times (1 + 8\%) = \$1501.85$
Ms. Li's commission will be $20.86. The cost will be $1501.85 after tax.

4 Ratios, Proportions, and Rates

Math Skills

1. 5:5
2. 5:10
3. 7:3
4. 4:2
5. 10:3
6. 1:10
7a. $21.12 ; 8
b. 260 ; 6
8. 0.79
9. 0.48
10. 3
11. 42
12. 12.25
13. 1.5

ISBN: 978-1-77149-206-5

Answers

Problem Solving

1a. $17.5 \; ; \; 17.5$

$\dfrac{2}{5} = \dfrac{9}{w}$

$2w = 5 \times 9$

$w = 22.5$

22.5

b. $\dfrac{2}{5} = \dfrac{1.5}{w}$

$2w = 5 \times 1.5$

$w = 3.75$

3.75

2a. • flour:

$\dfrac{300}{4} = \dfrac{w}{6}$

$4w = 300 \times 6$

$w = 450$

450

• milk:

$\dfrac{250}{4} = \dfrac{w}{6}$

$4w = 250 \times 6$

$w = 375$

375

• egg:

$\dfrac{2}{4} = \dfrac{w}{6}$

$4w = 2 \times 6$

$w = 3$

3

• water:

$\dfrac{100}{4} = \dfrac{w}{6}$

$4w = 100 \times 6$

$w = 150$

150

• butter:

$\dfrac{40}{4} = \dfrac{w}{6}$

$4w = 40 \times 6$

$w = 60$

60

b. $\dfrac{65}{2} = \dfrac{w}{6}$

$2w = 65 \times 6$

$w = 195$

195

3a. $\dfrac{15}{10} = \dfrac{37.5}{w}$

$15w = 10 \times 37.5$

$w = 25$

25

b. $\dfrac{15}{10} = \dfrac{l}{15}$

$10l = 15 \times 15$

$l = 22.5$

22.5

4a. $\dfrac{1.3}{1} = \dfrac{x}{20}$

$x = 1.3 \times 20$

$x = 26$

26

b. $\dfrac{1.3}{1} = \dfrac{13}{x}$

$1.3x = 1 \times 13$

$x = 10$

10

c. $\dfrac{1.3}{1} = \dfrac{11.05}{x}$

$1.3x = 1 \times 11.05$

$x = 8.5$

8.50

5a. $2:8 = 1:4$

The ratio of fertilizer to grass seeds is 1:4.

b. $1:4 = 2.5:10$

2.5 kg of fertilizer is needed.

6. $7:11 = 35:55$

35 of them were chocolate chip cookies.

7. $1:8 = 10:80$

Agatha needs to purchase 80 drinks.

8. $2:3 = 35:52.5$

Joey spends 52.5 min on swimming.

9a. $9:7 = 27:21$

Winnie's soccer team lost 21 games.

b. $9:7 = 18:14$

Winnie's soccer team won 18 games.

10a. base:height = 3:4 = 4.5:6 (Triangle A)

Yes, the triangles are similar.

b. base:hypotenuse = 3:5 ≠ 6:8 (Triangle B)

No, the triangles are not similar.

11a. $226.5 \div 3 = 75.5$

Marc's speed is 75.5 km/h.

b. $75.5 \times 5 = 377.5$

Marc will travel 377.5 km in total.

12. Apple Mart: $3.54 \div 6$ apples = $0.59/apple

Fresh Market: $4.32 \div 8$ apples = $0.54/apple

Fresh Market has the better deal.

13a. Rate: $4.15 \div 100$ g = $0.0415/g

Dried kiwis: $10.79 \div 0.0415 = 260$

260 g of dried kiwis can be bought.

b. $0.0415/g \times 340$ g = $14.11

340 g of dried kiwis cost $14.11.

14. Possible lengths:

$\dfrac{1.6}{2.4} = \dfrac{l}{12}$

$2.4l = 1.6 \times 12$

$l = 8$

$\dfrac{1.6}{2.4} = \dfrac{12}{l}$

$1.6l = 2.4 \times 12$

$l = 18$

The possible lengths of the other side are 8 cm and 18 cm.

15. New car: $150 \div 12 = 12.5$

Difference: $14.8 - 12.5 = 2.3$

Joe's new car is more fuel efficient by 2.3 km/L.

16a. Vinegar:

$\dfrac{30}{5} = \dfrac{v}{40}$

$5v = 30 \times 40$

$v = 240$

Water:

$16:4 = 960:240$

Camilla should add 960 mL of water.

b. baking soda to water = 40:960 = 1:24

The ratio of baking soda to water is 1:24.

c. baking soda to vinegar = 5:30 = 1:6

vinegar to water = 4:16 = 6:24

baking soda to vinegar to water = 1:6:24

baking soda to solution = 1:31 = 20:620

(baking soda + vinegar + water)

20 g of baking soda is needed.

5 Pythagorean Relationship

Math Skills

1.

ISBN: 978-1-77149-206-5

2a. 16 ; 25
  9
  9
  3

b. $2.5^2 + 6^2 = d^2$
  $42.25 = d^2$
  $\sqrt{42.25} = \sqrt{d^2}$
  $6.5 = d$

c. $4.5^2 + 6^2 = c^2$
  $56.25 = c^2$
  $\sqrt{56.25} = \sqrt{c^2}$
  $7.5 = c$

d. $5^2 + 12^2 = h^2$
  $169 = h^2$
  $\sqrt{169} = \sqrt{h^2}$
  $13 = h$

Problem Solving

  4 ; 9 ; 5 ; 5 ; 2.24 ; 2.24

1a. $r^2 + 1^2 = 3^2$
  $r^2 + 1 = 9$
  $r^2 = 8$
  $\sqrt{r^2} = \sqrt{8}$
  $r = 2.83$
  2.83

b. $r^2 + 2^2 = 4^2$
  $r^2 + 4 = 16$
  $r^2 = 12$
  $\sqrt{r^2} = \sqrt{12}$
  $r = 3.46$
  3.46

2. $w^2 = 5^2 + 28^2$
  $w^2 = 809$
  $\sqrt{w^2} = \sqrt{809}$
  $w = 28.44$
  28.44

3. $h^2 = 12^2 + (12 + 23)^2$
  $h^2 = 1369$
  $\sqrt{h^2} = \sqrt{1369}$
  $h = 37$
  37

4. $a^2 + 16.3^2 = 24.6^2$
  $a^2 + 265.69 = 605.16$
  $a^2 = 339.47$
  $\sqrt{a^2} = \sqrt{339.47}$
  $a = 18.42$
  18.42

5. $x^2 + x^2 = 26^2$
  $2x^2 = 676$
  $x^2 = 338$
  $\sqrt{x^2} = \sqrt{338}$
  $x = 18.38$
  18.38 ; 18.38

6. Side length of triangle: $60 \div 3 = 20$
  $e^2 + (20 \div 2)^2 = 20^2$
  $e^2 + 100 = 400$
  $e^2 = 300$
  $\sqrt{e^2} = \sqrt{300}$
  $e = 17.32$

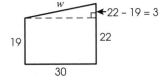

  Area: $20 \times 17.32 \div 2 = 173.2$
  173.2

7. $w^2 = 3^2 + 30^2$
  $w^2 = 909$
  $\sqrt{w^2} = \sqrt{909}$
  $w = 30.15$
  30.15

8. Fire hydrant:
  $d^2 = 9^2 + 40^2$
  $d^2 = 1681$
  $\sqrt{d^2} = \sqrt{1681}$
  $d = 41$

  Mailbox:
  $c^2 = 24^2 + 32^2$
  $c^2 = 1600$
  $\sqrt{c^2} = \sqrt{1600}$
  $c = 40$

  mailbox

9. $c^2 = 16^2 + 21^2$
  $c^2 = 697$
  $\sqrt{c^2} = \sqrt{697}$
  $c = 26.4$ ← not 26
  is not ; the sides of the triangle do not
  satisfy the Pythagorean theorem

10. $d^2 = 35^2 + 12^2$
  $d^2 = 1369$
  $\sqrt{d^2} = \sqrt{1369}$
  $d = 37$
  Vera and Simon are 37 m apart.

11. $d^2 = 2.5^2 + 4^2$
  $d^2 = 22.25$
  $\sqrt{d^2} = \sqrt{22.25}$
  $d = 4.72$
  The two ferries will be 4.72 km apart.

12a. $d^2 = 13^2 + 5^2$
  $d^2 = 194$
  $\sqrt{d^2} = \sqrt{194}$
  $d = 13.93$
  Regina's boat was 13.93 km away.

b. $d^2 = 13^2 + (5 + 6)^2$
  $d^2 = 290$
  $\sqrt{d^2} = \sqrt{290}$
  $d = 17.03$
  Difference: $17.03 - 13.93 = 3.1$
  It is now 3.1 km farther than before.

13. $f^2 = 20^2 + 8^2$
  $f^2 = 464$
  $\sqrt{f^2} = \sqrt{464}$
  $f = 21.54$
  The length of the fence will be 21.54 m.

14. Length of $\overline{AC}$:
  $x^2 = 4.5^2 + 9.7^2$
  $x^2 = 114.34$
  $\sqrt{x^2} = \sqrt{114.34}$
  $x = 10.69$

  Length of $\overline{BC}$:
  $y^2 = 3.8^2 + 9.7^2$
  $y^2 = 108.53$
  $\sqrt{y^2} = \sqrt{108.53}$
  $y = 10.42$

  Length of fence:
  $4.5 + 3.8 + 10.69 + 10.42 = 29.41$
  Ryan needs 29.41 m of fencing.

15. $s^2 + s^2 = 19.8^2$
  $2s^2 = 392.04$
  $s^2 = 196.02$
  $\sqrt{s^2} = \sqrt{196.02}$
  $s = 14$
  The side length of the square is 14 cm.

16. $x^2 = 11^2 + 15^2$
  $x^2 = 346$
  $\sqrt{x^2} = \sqrt{346}$
  $x = 18.6$

  $y^2 = 6^2 + 15^2$
  $y^2 = 261$
  $\sqrt{y^2} = \sqrt{261}$
  $y = 16.16$

  Perimeter: $11 + 6 + 18.6 + 16.16 = 51.76$
  The perimeter of the frame is 51.76 cm.

17a. Height of roof: $r^2 + (6 ÷ 2)^2 = 4.6^2$
$$r^2 + 9 = 21.16$$
$$r^2 = 12.16$$
$$\sqrt{r^2} = \sqrt{12.16}$$
$$r = 3.49$$
Height of house: $3.49 + 5 = 8.49$
The house is 8.49 m tall.

b. $6 × 3.49 ÷ 2 + 6 × 5 = 40.47$
The area of the front of the house is 40.47 m².

18. $a^2 + 45^2 = 75^2$
$$a^2 + 2025 = 5625$$
$$a^2 = 3600$$
$$\sqrt{a^2} = \sqrt{3600}$$
$$a = 60$$
Total trimmings: $45 × 2 + 60 × 2 = 210$
Kyle needs 210 cm of trimming.

19a. $x^2 = 17.4^2 + 17.4^2$ $y^2 = 24.61^2 + 24.61^2$
$$x^2 = 605.52$$ $$y^2 = 1211.3$$
$$\sqrt{x^2} = \sqrt{605.52}$$ $$\sqrt{y^2} = \sqrt{1211.3}$$
$$x = 24.61$$ $$y = 34.8$$
The lengths of x and y are 24.61 m and 34.8 m respectively.

b. $(17.4 + 34.8) × 17.4 ÷ 2 = 454.14$
The area of the trapezoid is 454.14 m².

20a. $b^2 + 18^2 = 27^2$
$$b^2 + 324 = 729$$
$$b^2 = 405$$
$$\sqrt{b^2} = \sqrt{405}$$ The bridge is 20.12 cm
$$b = 20.12$$ long.

b. $h^2 = 20.12^2 + (18 - 3)^2$
$$h^2 = 629.81$$
$$\sqrt{h^2} = \sqrt{629.81}$$
$$h = 25.1$$
Difference: $27 - 25.1 = 1.9$
The chain is 1.9 cm shorter.

21a. $s^2 = 6^2 + (14 - 6)^2$
$$s^2 = 100$$
$$\sqrt{s^2} = \sqrt{100}$$ The side length of the
$$s = 10$$ smaller square is 10 cm.

b. $a^2 + a^2 = 10^2$
$$2a^2 = 100$$
$$a^2 = 50$$
$$\sqrt{a^2} = \sqrt{50}$$
$$a = 7.07$$

Perimeter: $7.07 + 7.07 + 10 = 24.14$
The perimeter will be 24.14 cm.

22. Height of trapezoid:
$96.72 × 2 ÷ (5.4 + 5.4 + 5.4 + 4.6) = 9.3$
Left side: Right side:
$l^2 = 5.4^2 + 9.3^2$ $r^2 = 4.6^2 + 9.3^2$
$l^2 = 115.65$ $r^2 = 107.65$
$\sqrt{l^2} = \sqrt{115.65}$ $\sqrt{r^2} = \sqrt{107.65}$
$l = 10.75$ $r = 10.38$
Perimeter:
$5.4 + 5.4 + 5.4 + 4.6 + 10.75 + 10.38 = 41.93$
The perimeter of the trapezoid is 41.93 cm.

6   Circles

Math Skills

1. 10 ; 20 ; 10 ; 62.8 ; 10 ; 314
2. 3 cm ; 6 cm
   C = 2 × 3.14 × 3   A = 3.14 × 3²
     = 18.84 (cm)   = 28.26 (cm²)
3. A: 15.7 ; 19.625   B: 25.12 m ; 50.24 m²
   C: 12.56 cm ; 12.56 cm²
   D: 21.98 m ; 38.465 m²

Problem Solving

30 ; 15 ; 3.14 ; 15 ; 706.5 ; 706.5

1a. $3.14 × (30 + 5) = 3.14 × 35 = 109.9$; 109.9
b. Radius: $(30 + 5) ÷ 2 = 17.5$
   Area: $3.14 × 17.5^2 = 961.625$
   961.625

2a. $3.14 × 1.3 = 4.082$; 4.082
b. $2 × 3.14 × 0.55 = 3.454$; 3.454
3. $2 × 3.14 × 3.5 = 21.98$; 21.98
4. $2πr = 3.5$
   $r = 0.56$
   0.56

5a. $3.14 × 4^2 = 50.24$; 50.24
b. Radius: $12 ÷ 2 = 6$
   Area: $3.14 × 6^2 = 113.04$
   113.04
c. Small coaster: $2 × 3.14 × 4 = 25.12$
   Big coaster: $3.14 × 12 = 37.68$
   Rope: $25.12 + 37.68 = 62.8$
   62.8

6. Terry's pita: Terry's sister's pita:
   $2πr = 16$ Area: $3.14 × 5^2 = 78.5$
   $r = 2.55$
   Area: $3.14 × 2.55^2 = 20.42$
   Difference: $78.5 - 20.42 = 58.08$
   Terry's sister ; 58.08

ISBN: 978-1-77149-206-5

7. $0.1 \text{ m}^2 = 1000 \text{ cm}^2$
$\pi r^2 = 1000$
$r^2 = 318.47$
$r = 17.85$
Diameter: $2 \times 17.85 = 35.7$
The diameter of the mirror is 35.7 cm.

8. Entire coin:
Radius: $28 \div 2 = 14$
Area: $3.14 \times 14^2 = 615.44$
Inner circle:
Radius: $17 \div 2 = 8.5$
Area: $3.14 \times 8.5^2 = 226.865$
Outer ring: $615.44 - 226.865 = 388.575$
The area of the outer ring is 388.575 mm².

9. Area of square: $15 \times 15 = 225$
Area of circle: $3.14 \times (15 \div 2)^2 = 176.625$
Area of shaded parts: $225 - 176.625 = 48.375$
The total area is 48.375 cm².

10. $2\pi r = 57$
$r = 9.1$
Diameter: $2 \times 9.1 = 18.2$
Josephine's ring would be Size 8.

11. Small arc: $2 \times 3.14 \times 20 \div 4 = 31.4$
Big arc: $2 \times 3.14 \times 30 \div 4 = 47.1$
Length of track:
$31.4 + 47.1 + 30 \times 2 + 20 \times 2 = 178.5$
The track is 178.5 cm long.

12. Diameter of inner circle: $118 - 47 - 47 = 24$
Area of inner circle:
$3.14 \times (24 \div 2)^2 = 452.16$
Area of outer circle:
$3.14 \times (118 \div 2)^2 = 10\,930.34$
Area of label: $10\,930.34 - 452.16 = 10\,478.18$
The area of the label is 10 478.18 mm².

13a. Radius: $9.7 \div 2 = 4.85$
Area of semicircle: $3.14 \times 4.85^2 \div 2 = 36.93$
Width of rectangle: $15.2 - 4.85 - 4.85 = 5.5$
Area of rectangle: $5.5 \times 9.7 = 53.35$
Area of rink: $36.93 + 53.35 + 36.93 = 127.21$
The area of the skating rink is 127.21 m².

 b. Semicircle: $3.14 \times 9.7 \div 2 = 15.229$
Perimeter: $15.229 \times 2 + 5.5 \times 2 = 41.458$
The perimeter of the skating rink is 41.458 m.

14a. Circumference: $2 \times 3.14 \times 17.5 = 109.9$
Distance: $109.9 \times 100 = 10\,990 \text{ (cm)} = 109.9 \text{ (m)}$
The bike travels 109.9 m.

 b. Circumference: $3.14 \times 0.45 = 1.413$
No. of rotations: $141.3 \div 1.413 = 100$
The car's tire rotates 100 times.

15. Area: $3.14 \times (8 \div 2)^2 + 3.14 \times (11 \div 2)^2 = 145.225$
$\pi r^2 = 145.225$
$r^2 = 46.25$
$r = 6.8$
The radius of the large circle is 6.8 cm.

16a. $2\pi r = \pi$
$r = 0.5$
Area: $3.14 \times 0.5^2 = 0.785$
The area of the circle is 0.785 m².

 b. $2\pi r = 2\pi$
$r = 1$
Area: $3.14 \times 1^2 = 3.14$
Difference: $3.14 - 0.785 = 2.355$
The area will be 2.355 m² greater.

17. Small circumference: $3.14 \times 6.2 = 19.468$
Large circumference: $19.468 + 9.42 = 28.888$
Large radius: $2\pi r = 28.888$
$r = 4.6$
Area of small circle:
$3.14 \times (6.2 \div 2)^2 = 30.18$
Area of large circle: $3.14 \times 4.6^2 = 64.44$
Shaded area: $66.44 - 30.18 = 36.26$
The area of the shaded part is 36.26 cm².

18. The length is the diameter and the width is the radius.

$r \times 2r = 60.5$
$2r^2 = 60.5$
$\sqrt{r^2} = \sqrt{30.25}$
$r = 5.5$
Area of semicircle: $3.14 \times 5.5^2 \div 2 = 47.49$
The area of the semicircle is 47.49 cm².

19. Area of triangle: $(5 \times 2) \times 5 \div 2 = 25$
Area of circle: $3.14 \times 5^2 = 78.5$
Area not covered: $78.5 - 25 = 53.5$
The area of the circle not covered by the triangle is 53.5 cm².

20a. The perimeter of the star shape is equal to the four quarter-circumferences, or one full circumference of a circle. The side length of the square is the diameter.
Side length: $\sqrt{96.04} = 9.8$
Perimeter: $3.14 \times 9.8 = 30.772$
The perimeter of the star shape is 30.772 cm.

 b. Area of circle: $3.14 \times (9.8 \div 2)^2 = 75.39$
Area of star shape: $96.04 - 75.39 = 20.65$
The area of the star shape is 20.65 cm².

7   Volume and Surface Area
Math Skills

1. $V = 3.14 \times 3^2 \times 5 = 141.3 \text{ (cm}^3)$
S.A. $= 2 \times 3.14 \times 3^2 + 2 \times 3.14 \times 3 \times 5$
$= 150.72 \text{ (cm}^2)$

2. $V = \dfrac{4}{3} \times 3.14 \times 1^3 = 4.19 \text{ (cm}^3)$
S.A. $= 4 \times 3.14 \times 1^2 = 12.56 \text{ (cm}^2)$

3. $V = \dfrac{1}{3} \times 3.14 \times 2^2 \times 4 = 16.75$ (m³)
   S.A. $= 3.14 \times 2 \times 4.5 + 3.14 \times 2^2 = 40.82$ (m²)

4. $V = 3.14 \times (6 \div 2)^2 \times 20 = 565.2$ (m³)
   S.A. $= 2 \times 3.14 \times (6 \div 2)^2 + 2 \times 3.14 \times (6 \div 2) \times 20$
   $= 433.32$ (m²)

5A: $V = \dfrac{1}{3} \times 2 \times 2 \times 1.5 + 2 \times 2 \times 1 = 6$
   S.A. $= 2 \times 1.8 \div 2 \times 4 + 2 \times 1 \times 4 + 2 \times 2 = 19.2$
   6 m³ ; 19.2 m²

B: $V = \dfrac{1}{3} \times 3.14 \times 3.5^2 \times 7 + 3.14 \times 3.5^2 \times 5 = 282.08$
   S.A. $= 3.14 \times 3.5 \times 7.8 + 2 \times 3.14 \times 3.5 \times 5 + 3.14 \times 3.5^2$
   $= 234.087$
   282.08 cm³ ; 234.087 cm²

C: $V = 3 \times 2 \div 2 \times 3 + 3 \times 3 \times 2 = 27$
   S.A. $= 3 \times 2 \div 2 \times 2 + 2.5 \times 3 \times 2 + 3 \times 2 \times 4 + 3 \times 3 = 54$
   27 m³ ; 54 m²

Problem Solving

4 ; 12 ; 602.88 ; 602.88

1. $3.14 \times (7.8 \div 2)^2 \times 23 = 1098.47$; 1098.47

2a. $3.14 \times (2 \div 2)^2 \times 100 = 314$; 314
 b. $2 \times 3.14 \times 1^2 + 2 \times 3.14 \times 1 \times 100 = 634.28$
   634.28

3a. $3.14 \times (27 \div 2)^2 \times 13 + 3.14 \times (32 \div 2)^2 \times 21$
   $= 24\,320.085$
   24 320.085
 b. $3.14 \times 13.5^2 + 2 \times 3.14 \times 13.5 \times 13 = 1674.405$
   1674.405

4a. $\dfrac{1}{3} \times 3.14 \times 3^2 \times 8 = 75.36$ (cm³) $= 75.36$ (mL)
   75.36
 b. $3.14 \times 3 \times 8.5 = 80.07$; 80.07

5a. $\dfrac{1}{3} \times 3.14 \times (6 \div 2)^2 \times 10 = 94.2$
   94.2
 b. Side of cone: $\sqrt{3^2 + 10^2} = 10.44$
   $3.14 \times 3 \times 10.44 = 98.34$; 98.34

6a. $\dfrac{4}{3} \times 3.14 \times (24.26 \div 2)^3 = 7472.24$
   The volume is 7472.24 cm³.
 b. $4 \times 3.14 \times (24.26 \div 2)^2 = 1848.04$
   The surface area is 1848.04 cm².

7. Radius of red marble: $0.5 \times 2 = 1$
   Surface area: $4 \times 3.14 \times 1^2 = 12.56$
   The surface area is 12.56 cm².

8. Volume: $(1 - \dfrac{1}{4}) \times \dfrac{4}{3} \times 3.14 \times 4^3 = 200.96$
   Surface area:
   $(1 - \dfrac{1}{4}) \times 4 \times 3.14 \times 4^2 + 3.14 \times 4^2 = 200.96$
   The volume will be 200.96 cm³ and the surface area will be 200.96 cm².

9. $\dfrac{1}{3} \times 16 \times h = 50$
   $h = 9.375$
   The height is 9.375 cm.

10a. $\dfrac{1}{3} \times 30 \times 26 \times 42 = 10\,920$
   The volume of the pyramid is 10 920 cm³.
 b. Height of larger triangle:
   $\sqrt{42^2 + (26 \div 2)^2} = 43.97$
   Height of smaller triangle:
   $\sqrt{42^2 + (30 \div 2)^2} = 44.6$
   Surface area: $30 \times 43.97 \div 2 \times 2 + 26 \times 44.6$
   $\div 2 \times 2 + 30 \times 26 = 3258.7$
   The surface area is 3258.7 cm².

11. $6 \times 5.2 \div 2 \times 4 = 62.4$
   The surface area of the pyramid is 62.4 cm².

12a. $16 \times 15 \times 3.5 - (16 - 6) \times (15 \div 3) \times 3.5 \times 2$
   $= 490$
   The volume will be 490 cm³.
 b. $(16 \times 15 - 10 \times 5 \times 2) \times 2 + 15 \times 3.5 + 6 \times$
   $3.5 \times 2 + 5 \times 3.5 \times 3 + 10 \times 3.5 \times 2 = 497$
   The surface area will be 497 cm².

13a. $25 \times 10 \div 2 \times 14 + 25 \times 16 \times 14 = 7350$
   The volume of Amy's dollhouse is 7350 cm³.
 b. $25 \times 14 \times 10 + 25 \times 14 \times 16 = 9100$
   The volume of Ruby's dollhouse is 9100 cm³.

14. $11 \times 11 \times 4.5 - 3.14 \times (9 \div 2)^2 \times 4.5 = 258.37$
   The volume is 258.37 cm³.

15a. $3.14 \times (11.3 \div 2)^2 \times 17.5 \div 2 = 877.07$
   The volume of the cake is 877.07 cm³.
 b. $(2 \times 3.14 \times 5.65^2 + 2 \times 3.14 \times 5.65 \times 17.5) \div 2$
   $= 410.7$
   The total area covered will be 410.7 cm².

16a. Volume of cylinder: $3.14 \times (10 \div 2)^2 \times 12 = 942$
   Volume of cones:
   $\dfrac{1}{3} \times 3.14 \times (10 \div 2)^2 \times (12 \div 2) \times 2 = 314$
   Difference: $942 - 314 = 628$
   The volume has reduced by 628 cm³.
 b. Surface area of cylinder:
   $2 \times 3.14 \times 5^2 + 2 \times 3.14 \times 5 \times 12 = 533.8$
   Surface area of cones:
   $3.14 \times 5 \times 7.81 \times 2 = 245.234$
   Difference: $533.8 - 245.234 = 288.566$
   It has decreased by 288.566 cm².

17. $3.14 \times (24 \div 2)^2 \times 2 - 3.14 \times (9 \div 2)^2 \times 2 = 777.15$
   The volume of the washer is 777.15 mm³.

8 Angles and Triangles

Math Skills

1. 120° ; 60° ; 120°   2. 55° ; 75° ; 50°
3. 80° ; 60° ; 40°   4. 66° ; 66° ; 48°
5. $\overline{MO}$; ∠MON ; ∠OMN ; MON ; ASA
6. $\overline{DE}$; $\overline{DF}$; $\overline{EF}$; △DEF ; SSS

ISBN: 978-1-77149-206-5

7. $\overline{UW}$; $\angle UWV$; $\overline{VW}$; $\triangle UVW$; SAS

Problem Solving

135° ; 135° ; 45° ; 135° ; 135° ; 45°

1a. By supplementary angles: $a + 60° = 180°$
$a = 120°$
120°

b. By complementary angles: $b + 60° = 90°$
$b = 30°$
By supplementary angles: $c + 30° = 180°$
$c = 150°$
30° ; 150°

2a. By opposite angles: $\angle COD = 110°$; 110°

b. By supplementary angles:
$\angle AOC + 110° = 180°$
$\angle AOC = 70°$
70°

c. By isosceles triangle: $\angle ABO = \angle BAO$
By angles in a triangle:
$\angle ABO + \angle BAO + 110° = 180°$
$2 \times \angle ABO = 70°$
$\angle ABO = 35°$
35°

d. By isosceles triangle: $\angle OAC = \angle OCA$
By angles in a triangle:
$\angle OAC + \angle OCA + 70° = 180°$
$2 \times \angle OAC = 110°$
$\angle OAC = 55°$
55°

3a. $5a = 360°$
$a = 72°$
72°

b. Each triangle is an isosceles triangle.
By angles in a triangle: $72° + b + b = 180°$
$2b = 108°$
$b = 54°$
72° ; 54° ; 54°

4a. By alternate angles: $\angle BAD = \angle ADE = 57°$
57°

b. By alternate angles: $\angle BCA = \angle CAE = 49°$
$\angle DAE = \angle CAE - \angle CAD = 49° - 36° = 13°$
By angles in a triangle: $\angle DEA + 13° + 57° = 180°$
$\angle DEA = 110°$
$\angle BAC = \angle BAD - \angle CAD = 57° - 36° = 21°$
By angles in a triangle: $\angle CBA + 21° + 49° = 180°$
$\angle CBA = 110°$
Yes ; are ; 110° ; 110°.

5a. By supplementary angles:
$\angle PQO + 115° = 180°$
$\angle PQO = 65°$
By angles in a triangle:
$\angle POQ + 70° + 65° = 180°$
$\angle POQ = 45°$
By supplementary angles:
$\angle ONR + 134° = 180°$
$\angle ONR = 46°$
$\angle POQ \neq \angle ONR$
The levels are not parallel.

b. By angles in a triangle:
$\angle PMS + 70° + 65° = 180°$
$\angle PMS = 45°$
Level 1: $\angle PMS \neq \angle ONR$
Level 2: $\angle PMS = \angle POQ = 45°$
Level 2 is parallel to the ground.

6a.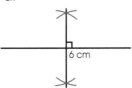
b.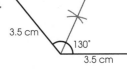
Each bisected angle is 30°.
Each bisected angle is 65°.

7a.
b.
The angle is 90°.
The angle is 90°.

8.
The smallest bisected angle is 22.5°.

9a.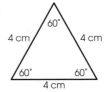
b.

c. d.

e.

The sizes will be 30°, 60°, and 90°.

ISBN: 978-1-77149-206-5

f. Yes, the triangles from (b) and (c) are congruent. Their side lengths are 4 cm, 4 cm, and 2.7 cm. Their angles are 70°, 70°, and 40°.

10. $(8 + 6 + 4) \times 2 - (8 \div 2) \times 2 = 28$
The perimeter of the shape is 28 cm.

11a. All the sides of a square are equal.
$\overline{WY} = \overline{ZX}$; $\overline{WX} = \overline{ZY}$; $\overline{XY} = \overline{YX}$
$\triangle WXY \cong \triangle ZYX$ (SSS)

b. $\overline{WY} = \overline{ZX}$; $\angle YWX = \angle XZY = 90°$; $\overline{WX} = \overline{ZY}$
$\triangle WXY \cong \triangle ZYX$ (SAS)

c. $\overline{WY}$ is parallel to $\overline{ZX}$.
$\overline{WX}$ is parallel to $\overline{ZY}$.
By alternate angles: $\angle WXY = \angle ZYX$
$\overline{XY} = \overline{YX}$
By alternate angles: $\angle WYX = \angle ZXY$
$\triangle WXY \cong \triangle ZYX$ (ASA)

12. Marcus's triangle: Nancy's triangle:

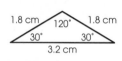 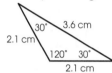

No, the triangles are not congruent.

13a. $\overline{AE} = \overline{DE}$
By opposite angles: $\angle AEB = \angle DEC$
$\overline{EB} = \overline{EC}$
$\triangle ABE \cong \triangle DCE$ (SAS)
Yes, they are congruent.

b. Since $\triangle ABE \cong \triangle DCE$, so $\overline{AB} = \overline{DC}$.
Yes, they are equal.

c. $\overline{AC} = \overline{AE} + \overline{EC} = \overline{DE} + \overline{EB} = \overline{DB}$
$\overline{AB} = \overline{DC}$; $\overline{BC} = \overline{CB}$
$\triangle ABC \cong \triangle DCB$ (SSS)
Yes, they are congruent.

14a. By alternate angles: $\angle AXY = \angle ZYX$
$\overline{XY} = \overline{YX}$
By alternate angles: $\angle XYA = \angle YXZ$
$\triangle AXY \cong \triangle ZYX$ (ASA)
Yes, they are congruent.

b. By corresponding angles: $\angle XBZ = \angle YZC$
Z is the midpoint of $\overline{BC}$, so $\overline{BZ} = \overline{ZC}$.
By corresponding angles: $\angle XZB = \angle YCZ$
$\triangle BXZ \cong \triangle ZYC$ (ASA)
Yes, they are congruent.

9 Cartesian Coordinate Plane

Math Skills

1. A(-2,4) ; B(-4,3) ;
C(0,0)
P(4,-4) ; Q(6,-4) ;
R(6,-6) ; S(2,-6)
W(-6,-1) ; X(-3,-1) ;
Y(-1,-3) ; Z(-4,-3)

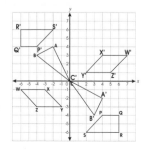

2a. A'(4,-2) ; B'(3,-4) ; C'(0,0)
b. P'(-4,4) ; Q'(-6,4) ; R'(-6,6) ; S'(-2,6)
c. W'(7,3) ; X'(4,3) ; Y'(2,1) ; Z'(5,1)

3a. Shape W'X'Y'Z'   b. Shape P'Q'R'S'
c. none   d. Shape A'B'C'

Problem Solving

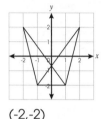 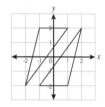

(-2,-2)

1a. (-1,2)
2a,c.

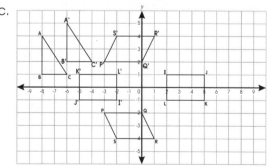

b. $2 \times 4 \div 2 = 4$; 4

b. • carrots:
Perimeter:
$(3 + 4) \times 2 = 14$
Area: $3 \times 4 = 12$
14 ; 12
• peas:
Perimeter:
$2+3+5+\sqrt{3^2+3^2}=14.24$
Area:
$(2 + 5) \times 3 \div 2 = 10.5$
14.24 ; 10.5
• peppers:
Perimeter:
$(\sqrt{1^2+3^2}+5)\times2=16.32$
Area: $5 \times 3 = 15$
16.32 ; 15

d. • carrots: (0,-3), (0,-7), (3,-3), (3,-7)
• peas: (-3,8), (-3,6), (0,8), (0,3)
• peppers: (1,2), (1,7), (4,1), (4,6)

e. The carrots enclosure will have fertilizer.

f. • Quadrant I: The peppers enclosure is transformed to Quadrant I.
• Quadrant IV: The carrots enclosure is transformed to Quadrant IV.

3a-c.

a. A'(-6,5) ; B'(-6,2) ; C'(-4,2)
Translate it 2 units to the right and 1 unit up.

b. I'(-2,-1) ; J'(-5,-1) ; K'(-5,1) ; L'(-2,1)
Rotate it 180° about (0,0).

ISBN: 978-1-77149-206-5

c. $P'(-3,2)$; $Q'(0,2)$; $R'(1,4)$; $S'(-2,4)$
Reflect it in the x-axis.

d. • Area: $2 \times 3 \div 2 = 3$
Perimeter: $2 + 3 + \sqrt{2^2 + 3^2} = 8.61$
The area is 3 square units and the perimeter is 8.61 units.
• Area: $2 \times 3 = 6$
Perimeter: $(3 + 2) \times 2 = 10$
The area is 6 square units and the perimeter is 10 units.
• Area: $3 \times 2 = 6$
Perimeter: $(3 + \sqrt{1^2 + 2^2}) \times 2 = 10.47$
The area is 6 square units and the perimeter is 10.47 units.

e. The triangle and its image both lie in Quadrant II.

f. The rectangle's image lies on the x-axis. The points (-5,0) and (-2,0) lie on the x-axis.

g. The parallelogram's image lies on the y-axis. The points (0,2) and (0,4) lie on the y-axis.

4. Original coordinates: (-2,2), (2,2), (-3,-2), (2,-2)
a. (-5,2), (-1,2), (-6,-2), (-1,-2)
b. (1,4), (5,4), (0,0), (5,0)
c. (-4,-1), (0,-1), (-5,-5), (0,-5)

5a. They will be (4,-6), (3,2), (-2,-8), (-1,0).
b. They will be (-4,6), (-3,-2), (2,8), (1,0).

6a. He translated it 3 units to the right and 2 units down.
b. He reflected it in the x-axis.
c. She rotated it 180° about (0,0).
d. He translated it 6 units to the left and 3 units up, and then rotated it 90° clockwise about (0,0).
e. Side length: $5 - 1 = 4$
Area: $4 \times 4 = 16$
The shape is a square. The area of the shape is 16 square units.

7a. Reflection: (2,-4)
Distance: $2 - (-2) = 4$
The distance is 4 units.
b. Rotation: (2,4)
Distance: $\sqrt{(2 - (-2))^2 + (4 - (-4))^2} = 8.94$
The distance is 8.94 units.

10 Polynomials and Equations

Math Skills

1a. $7x + 7$ b. $4x$ c. $6x^3$
d. $-12x^3y^3$ e. $8m^3$ f. $0.25s$
g. $3b$ h. $-3x^{-1}y^3$ i. $7m^7n^{-3}$
j. $\frac{1}{2}p^{-7}$ k. $4x^2y - 8xy + 6y^2$
l. $-8ab + 4bc - 6ac$

2a. $-2c - 3c = 7 - 22$
$-5c = -15$
$c = 3$

b. $10t - 30 = 16$
$10t = 46$
$t = 4.6$

c. $6k + 2 = -4k - 12$
$6k + 4k = -12 - 2$
$10k = -14$
$k = -1.4$

d. $-2t - 1 = 3(4t + 2)$
$-2t - 1 = 12t + 6$
$-2t - 12t = 6 + 1$
$-14t = 7$
$t = -0.5$

e. $4(3m+1) = 6m-2$
$12m+4 = 6m-2$
$12m-6m = -2-4$
$6m = -6$
$m = -1$

f. $2(4r - 1) = (3r + \frac{1}{3}) \times 3$
$8r - 2 = 9r + 1$
$8r - 9r = 1 + 2$
$-r = 3$
$r = -3$

g. $0.6t = 1.5t + 1.8$
$0.6t - 1.5t = 1.8$
$-0.9t = 1.8$
$t = -2$

h. $1.3u - 14.3 = 15.8 - 2.2u$
$1.3u + 2.2u = 15.8 + 14.3$
$3.5u = 30.1$
$u = 8.6$

i. $5(u + 3) = 3(7 - u)$
$5u + 15 = 21 - 3u$
$5u + 3u = 21 - 15$
$8u = 6$
$u = 0.75$

Problem Solving

$8 ; 4 ; 8 ; 136 ; 17 ; 17$

1. $(2w + w) \times 2 = 6$
$6w = 6$
$w = 1$
1

2. $3b - 7 = 20$
$3b = 27$
$b = 9$
9

3. $4(1.5h + 6) = 30$
$6h + 24 = 30$
$6h = 6$
$h = 1$
1

4. $a + a + a + 0.5 + 1.3 = 5.4$
$3a = 3.6$
$a = 1.2$
1.2

5. $\frac{1}{4} \times 2w \times w = 8$
$\frac{1}{2}w^2 = 8$
$w^2 = 16$
$\sqrt{w^2} = \sqrt{16}$
$w = 4$
4

6. $2(t - 3) + 4 = t + 5$
$2t - 6 + 4 = t + 5$
$2t - t = 5 + 6 - 4$
$t = 7$
7

7. $5(x + 0.5 + 3x + 4x - 0.3) = 13$
$8x + 0.2 = 2.6$
$8x = 2.4$
$x = 0.3$
$x + 0.5 = 0.8$ $3x = 0.9$ $4x - 0.3 = 0.9$
$0.8 ; 0.9 ; 0.9$

ISBN: 978-1-77149-206-5

8a. $8.5t = 17.5 + 6.75t$ b. $8.5t = 17.5 + 6.75t + 28$
     $1.75t = 17.5$ $1.75t = 45.5$
        $t = 10$ $t = 26$
        10   26

9a. $4a = (a + 6 + 0.7a) \times 2$
    $4a = (1.7a + 6) \times 2$
    $4a = 3.4a + 12$
   $0.6a = 12$
     $a = 20$
   Perimeter: $(20 + 6 + 0.7 \times 20) \times 2 = 80$
   The perimeter is 80 m.

b. $a^2 = (a + 6) \times 0.7a$
          $a^2 = 0.7a^2 + 4.2a$
      $0.3a^2 = 4.2a$
  $0.3a^2 \div 0.3a = 4.2a \div 0.3a$
          $a = 14$
   Area: $a^2 = 14^2 = 196$
   The area was 196 m².

10a. Let s be the side length of the big square.
    $s^2 - 4 \times (\frac{s}{5})^2 = 525$
    $s^2 - \frac{4}{25}s^2 = 525$
    $\frac{21}{25}s^2 = 525$
      $s^2 = 625$ The area of the big
       $s = 25$ square was 625 cm².

b. $2s + 18(\frac{s}{5}) = 2 \times 25 + 18 \times (\frac{25}{5}) = 140$
   The perimeter of the shape is 140 cm.

11a. $6 \times 0.65 + 5d + 2.05 = 10 \times 0.65 + 3d + 4.75$
           $5d + 5.95 = 3d + 11.25$
               $2d = 5.3$
                $d = 2.65$
   A drink cost $2.65.

b. $(6 \times 0.65 + 5d + 2.05) \times 2$
  $= (6 \times 0.65 + 5 \times 2.65 + 2.05) \times 2 = 38.4$
   Laura and Lindsay had $38.40 altogether.

12a. Let r be Roger's score.
       $2r - 1 = (3r + 2) \div 2$
   $(2r - 1) \times 2 = (3r + 2) \div 2 \times 2$
      $4r - 2 = 3r + 2$
           $r = 4$ Roger scored 4 points.

b. $r + 2r - 1 + 3r + 2 = 13$
             $6r = 12$
              $r = 2$
   Steve: $2 \times 2 - 1 = 3$ Tyler: $3 \times 2 + 2 = 8$
   Roger scored 2 points, Steve scored
   3 points, and Tyler scored 8 points.

13a. $81.25 = 10^2 - 3w \times w$
   $81.25 = 100 - 3w^2$
     $3w^2 = 18.75$
      $w^2 = 6.25$ The width of the
       $w = 2.5$ walkway is 2.5 m.

b. $(2.5 \times 3 + 2.5 + 2.5 \times 3) \times c = 245$
             $17.5c = 245$
                $c = 14$
   Each metre of fencing is $14.

14a. Let l be the number of loonies.
   $2 \times 2l + 1 \times l + 0.25 \times \frac{1}{2}l = 20.5$
                $5.125l = 20.5$
                   $l = 4$
   Anthony has 4 loonies.

b. $2l + l + \frac{1}{2}l = 2 \times 4 + 4 + \frac{1}{2} \times 4 = 14$
   Anthony has 14 coins in all.

c. $2 \times 2l - 0.25 \times \frac{1}{2}l = 2 \times 8 - 0.25 \times 2 = 15.5$
   Anthony has $15.50 more in toonies than
   in quarters.

15. Let e be the length of the extension.
   $(4.5 + 4.5 + e) \times 2 - 4.5 \times 4 = 1.2$
         $(9 + e) \times 2 - 18 = 1.2$
          $18 + 2e - 18 = 1.2$
                $2e = 1.2$
                 $e = 0.6$
   Area: $(4.5 + 0.6) \times 4.5 = 22.95$
   The area is 22.95 m².

16. $1.5 \times 60 = (1.5 - t) \times (60 + 15)$
         $90 = 112.5 - 75t$
      $75t = 22.5$
        $t = 0.3$
   It would be 0.3 h faster.

17a.   3 lemons = 2 apples = 5 limes
   3 oranges = 5 limes + 4 limes
   3 oranges = 9 limes
   1 orange = 3 limes
   3 limes equal the weight of 1 orange.

b. 4 apples = 3 lemons + 5 limes
   3 oranges = 3 lemons + 4 limes
   Difference: 1 lime
   1 lime is needed.

c. $3 \times 0.18 = 3 \times 0.1 + 4l$
      $0.54 = 0.3 + 4l$
      $0.24 = 4l$ The weight of a lime
         $l = 0.06$ is 0.06 kg.

11 Inequalities

Math Skills

1a. 3 ; 8   b. 0 ; 0.5   c. 5 ; 4.5
 d. -6   e. 1 ; -0.5   f. 3.8 ; 6.3 ; 0.7
 g. -1   h. -3 ; -4   i. 1 ; -4 ; 0

2a. $2x \div 2 > 4 \div 2$ b. $2 - w - 2 < 3 - 2$
        $x > 2$ $-w < 1$
   B $w > -1$
                       A

ISBN: 978-1-77149-206-5

c. $3y \le 9$
   $y \le 3$
   A

d. $2 \ge 2m$
   $1 \ge m$
   B

e. $-5v \div (-5) > 25 \div (-5)$
   $v > -5$
   B

f. $24 \ge -6z$
   $24 \div (-6) \le -6z \div (-6)$
   $-4 \le z$
   B

Problem Solving

-2 ; -2 ; -2 ; (Suggested answers) -3 ; -4

1a. $j - 3 > 6$ The only number from -10 to 10
    $j > 9$ that is greater than 9 is 10.
    10

b. $3a < -27$ The only number from -10 to 10
   $a < -9$ that is less than -9 is -10.
   -10

2. $2s - 6 > 0$
   $2s > 6$
   $s > 3$
   greater than ; 3

3. $d + 12 < 30$
   $d < 18$
   less than ; 18

4a. $2q + 3 \times 2 \ge 50$
    $2q + 6 \ge 50$
    $2q \ge 44$
    $q \ge 22$
    at least ; 22

b. $2 \times 21 + 3q > 90$
   $42 + 3q > 90$
   $3q > 48$
   $q > 16$
   more than ; 16

5. $40m \ge 200$
   $m \ge 5$
   at least ; 5

6. $4w + 3 > 5$
   $4w > 2$
   $w > 0.5$
   more than ; 0.5

7a. $126 \div x \ge 18$
    $126 \ge 18x$
    $7 \ge x$
    at most ; 7

b. $126 \div x \le 14$
   $126 \le 14x$
   $9 \le x$
   at least ; 9

8. $4(38 - d) < 100$
   $152 - 4d < 100$
   $52 < 4d$
   $13 < d$
   The discount is more than $13.

9. $(5 + 2t) \div 3 > -1$
   $5 + 2t > -3$
   $2t > -8$
   $t > -4$
   The temperature of the two cities is greater than -4°C.

10a. $3m - 1 > 2m + 5$
     $m > 6$
     Micah is more than 6 years old.

b. $3m - 1 + 2m + 5 < 44$
   $5m + 4 < 44$
   $5m < 40$
   $m < 8$
   Micah's age: $6 < m < 8$
   Micah is 7 years old.

11a. $5 \times (5 + x) \le 40$
     $25 + 5x \le 40$
     $5x \le 15$
     $x \le 3$
     Length of court: $5 + x \le 8$
     The length of the court is at most 8 m.

b. Perimeter: $(5 + 5 + x) \times 2 = 20 + 2x$
   $x \le 3$
   $2x \le 6$
   $20 + 2x \le 26$
   The perimeter of the court is at most 26 m.

5 m

$(5 + x)$ m

12a. $220 - 4p > 15p + 11$
     $209 > 19p$
     $11 > p$
     There could be less than 11 passengers.

b. $11 > 220 \div c$
   $c > 220 \div 11$
   $c > 20$
   The train has more than 20 cabins.

13a. $6x - 2 \times 3 > 4(x + 4)$
     $6x - 6 > 4x + 16$
     $2x > 22$
     $x > 11$
     $x + 4 > 15$
     The length of Room A is greater than 15 m.

b. Difference in area:
   $(6x - 2 \times 3) - 4(x + 4)$
   $= 6x - 6 - (4x + 16) = 2x - 22$
   $x < 15$
   $2x < 30$
   $2x - 22 < 30 - 22$
   $2x - 22 < 8$
   The difference in area is less than 8 m².

14. $30 - 4b \ge 6$
    $24 \ge 4b$
    $6 \ge b$

    $7b - 30 \ge 5$
    $7b \ge 35$
    $b \ge 5$

    $6 \ge b \ge 5$
    There are 5 or 6 blocks in each tower.

15. Let c be the length of the shorter swabs.
    $(3(c + 5) + 2c) \div 5 < 60$
    $3c + 15 + 2c < 300$
    $5c < 285$
    $c < 57$
    $c + 5 < 62$
    c must be between 50 and 60.
    No, it cannot be certain.

16. $11.2 \div d > 3.2$
    $11.2 \div 3.2 > d$
    $3.5 > d$ ← cannot buy 3.5 doughnuts
    Aaron can buy at most 3 doughnuts.

ISBN: 978-1-77149-206-5

17. $-2(x + 8) + 20 > 0$
$-2(x + 8) > -20$
$-2(x + 8) \div (-2) < -20 \div (-2)$
$x + 8 < 10$
$x < 2$
$-32 > -4(x + 10)$
$-32 \div (-4) < -4(x + 10) \div (-4)$
$8 < x + 10$
$-2 < x$
No, Susie is incorrect.

18. $5s < 6000 \div 2$
$5s < 3000$
$s < 600$
Daryl saved less than $600 each year.

19a. $20 < 2p < 24$
$20 < 2p$ $2p < 24$
$10 < p$ $p < 12$
          $10 < p < 12$
The temperature of the first bowl was between 10°C and 12°C.

b. $20 < p - 8 < 24$
$20 < p - 8$ $p - 8 < 24$
$28 < p$ $p < 32$
          $28 < p < 32$
The temperature of the second bowl was between 28°C and 32°C.

20. $3 < 9 - 2c < 7$
$3 < 9 - 2c$ $9 - 2c < 7$
$2c < 6$ $2 < 2c$
$c < 3$ $1 < c$
          $1 < c < 3$
The length is between 1 cm and 3 cm.

12   Graphs and Relations

Math Skills

1. 3 ; 4 ; 5   -5 ; -1 ; 3   13 ; 11 ; 9
2. 2 ; 2   1 ; 2   -2 ; 3
3a. $\dfrac{4 - 1}{3 - 1} = \dfrac{3}{2}$ $\dfrac{3 - 1}{5 - 9} = -\dfrac{2}{4}$

b. The slope of $\overline{AB}$ is steeper than the slope of $\overline{CD}$. They run in opposite directions.

Problem Solving

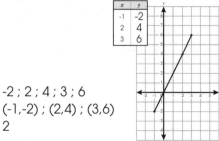

x	y
-1	-2
2	4
3	6

-2 ; 2 ; 4 ; 3 ; 6
(-1,-2) ; (2,4) ; (3,6)
2

1a. The y-coordinate is 3.
  b. The x-coordinate is 2.5.

2a. • Slope of $\overline{MN}$: $\dfrac{5 - (-1)}{4 - 2} = \dfrac{6}{2} = 3$
The slope of $\overline{MN}$ is 3.
• Slope of $\overline{OP}$: $\dfrac{3 - 1}{7 - 13} = -\dfrac{2}{6} = -\dfrac{1}{3}$
The slope of $\overline{OP}$ is $-\dfrac{1}{3}$.
• Slope of $\overline{QR}$: $\dfrac{3 - (-1)}{1 - (-3)} = \dfrac{4}{4} = 1$
The slope of $\overline{QR}$ is 1.

b. It means that as the x-coordinate increases, the y-coordinate decreases.

c. A slope that has a greater positive value means that the line is steeper.

d. $\overline{MN}$: The x-coordinate is 3.
$\overline{OP}$: The x-coordinate is 10.
$\overline{QR}$: The x-coordinate is 0.

e. Try (1,3) by substituting 1 for x into the relation.
$x + 3 = 1 + 3 = 4$
The y-coordinate of the relation is not 3.
No, she is incorrect.

f. • $y = 3x - 7$:
Try (4,5) for $\overline{MN}$.
$3x - 7 = 3(4) - 7 = 5$
The y-coordinate of the relation is 5.
The relation describes $\overline{MN}$.

• $y = x + 2$:
Try (1,3) for $\overline{QR}$.
$x + 2 = 1 + 2 = 3$
The y-coordinate of the relation is 3.
The relation describes $\overline{QR}$.

3a. Slope $= \dfrac{3 - 0}{5 - (-1)} = \dfrac{3}{6} = \dfrac{1}{2}$
The slope is $\dfrac{1}{2}$.

b. It is 2.
It is 2.5.

c. Slope $= \dfrac{1 - (-4)}{-4 - 1} = -\dfrac{5}{5} = -1$
The slope is -1.

d. It is -3.
It is -1.

e. $\overline{CD}$ is steeper.

f. $\overline{AB}$ touches the x-axis at (-1,0) and the y-axis at (0,0.5). $\overline{CD}$ touches the x-axis at (-3,0) and the y-axis at (0,-3).

4a. 6 ; 5 ; 3
b. -6 ; -2 ; 2
c. -5 ; -4.5 ; -4

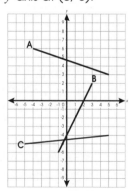

ISBN: 978-1-77149-206-5

d. $-\frac{1}{3}x + 4\frac{2}{3} = -\frac{1}{3}(1.2) + 4\frac{2}{3} = 4\frac{4}{15}$

   The value of y is $4\frac{4}{15}$.

e. Line A: Slope $= \frac{6-3}{-4-5} = -\frac{3}{9} = -\frac{1}{3}$

   Line B: Slope $= \frac{2-(-2)}{3-1} = \frac{4}{2} = 2$

   Line C: Slope $= \frac{-4-(-5)}{5-(-5)} = \frac{1}{10}$

   The slopes are $-\frac{1}{3}$, 2, $\frac{1}{10}$ for Lines A, B, and C respectively.

5a. Escalator A: Escalator B:

   $2y + x = 12$ $2y + 4 = x$

   $2y = -x + 12$ $2y = x - 4$

   $y = -\frac{1}{2}x + 6$ $y = \frac{1}{2}x - 2$

b.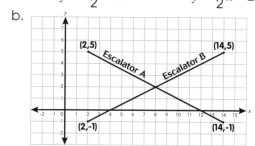

c. The escalators intersect at (8,2).

d. Escalator A: Escalator B:

   $\frac{5-(-1)}{2-14} = -\frac{6}{12} = -\frac{1}{2}$ $\frac{5-(-1)}{14-2} = \frac{6}{12} = \frac{1}{2}$

   The escalators' slopes have the same steepness but run in opposite directions.

6a. Section 1: $\frac{1-(-3)}{-1-4} = -\frac{4}{5}$

   Section 2: $\frac{3-1}{3-(-1)} = \frac{2}{4} = \frac{1}{2}$

   Section 3: $\frac{7-3}{-1-3} = -\frac{4}{4} = -1$

   Section 3 has the steepest slope.

b. $\frac{7-(-3)}{-1-4} = -\frac{10}{5} = -2$

   The slope would have been -2.

7a. $\frac{6-2}{5-(-1)} = \frac{4}{6} = \frac{2}{3}$

   The slope is $\frac{2}{3}$.

b. Try (5,6).

   $\frac{2}{3}x + 2\frac{2}{3} = \frac{2}{3}(5) + 2\frac{2}{3} = 6$

   Yes, it describes the route.

   Try $(3, 4\frac{2}{3})$.

   $\frac{2}{3}(3) + 2\frac{2}{3} = 4\frac{2}{3}$

   Yes, it is on the route.

c. x-coordinate: $((-1) + 5) \div 2 = 2$

   y-coordinate: $(2 + 6) \div 2 = 4$

   The coordinates are (2,4).

13 Probability

   does not affect ; affects

1a. IE ; DE   b. IE ; IE   c. IE ; IE ; DE

Problem Solving

$\frac{3}{5}$; $\frac{2}{5}$; $\frac{3}{5}$; $\frac{2}{5}$; $\frac{6}{25}$; $\frac{6}{25}$

1a. P(blue marble and red clip)

   = P(blue marble) × P(red clip)

   $= \frac{2}{5} \times \frac{3}{5}$

   $= \frac{6}{25}$

   $\frac{6}{25}$

b. P(red marble and red clip)

   = P(red marble) × P(red clip)

   $= \frac{3}{5} \times \frac{3}{5}$

   $= \frac{9}{25}$

   $\frac{9}{25}$

2a. $P(A) \times P(A) = \frac{1}{4} \times \frac{1}{4} = \frac{1}{16}$

   The probability is $\frac{1}{16}$.

b. $P(B) \times P(D) = \frac{1}{4} \times \frac{1}{4} = \frac{1}{16}$

   The probability is $\frac{1}{16}$.

c. P(vowel) × P(vowel) $= \frac{1}{4} \times \frac{1}{4} = \frac{1}{16}$

   The probability is $\frac{1}{16}$.

d. $P(A) \times P(C) = \frac{1}{4} \times \frac{2}{4} = \frac{1}{8}$

   The probability is $\frac{1}{8}$.

e. P(vowel) × P(consonant) $= \frac{1}{4} \times \frac{3}{4} = \frac{3}{16}$

   The probability is $\frac{3}{16}$.

f. P(consonant) × P(consonant)

   $= \frac{3}{4} \times \frac{3}{4} = \frac{9}{16}$

   The probability is $\frac{9}{16}$.

g. • P(picking B) × P(spinning C) $= \frac{1}{4} \times \frac{2}{4} = \frac{1}{8}$

   The probability is $\frac{1}{8}$.

   • P(picking a consonant) × P(spinning a vowel)

   $= \frac{3}{4} \times \frac{1}{4} = \frac{3}{16}$

   The probability is $\frac{3}{16}$.

h. The events are dependent because the probability of spinning the letter depends on the outcome of the ball picked.

ISBN: 978-1-77149-206-5

3a. • P(1 on red) × P(6 on blue) $= \frac{1}{6} \times \frac{1}{6} = \frac{1}{36}$
The probability is $\frac{1}{36}$.
• P(2 on red) × P(even on blue) $= \frac{1}{6} \times \frac{3}{6} = \frac{1}{12}$
The probability is $\frac{1}{12}$.
• P(odd on red) × P(odd on blue) $= \frac{3}{6} \times \frac{3}{6} = \frac{1}{4}$
The probability is $\frac{1}{4}$.
• P(5 or 6 on red) × P(1 on blue) $= \frac{2}{6} \times \frac{1}{6} = \frac{1}{18}$
The probability is $\frac{1}{18}$.

b.

+	1	2	3	4	5	6
1	2	3	4	5	6	7
2	3	4	5	6	7	8
3	4	5	6	7	8	9
4	5	6	7	8	9	10
5	6	7	8	9	10	11
6	7	8	9	10	11	12

• $\frac{3}{36} = \frac{1}{12}$; The probability is $\frac{1}{12}$.
• $\frac{15}{36} = \frac{5}{12}$; The probability is $\frac{5}{12}$.

c. $(2 + 3 \times 2 + 4 \times 3 + 5 \times 4 + 6 \times 5 + 7 \times 6 + 8 \times 5 + 9 \times 4 + 10 \times 3 + 11 \times 2 + 12) \div 36 = 7$
The average of the outcomes is 7.

4a. Since Ashley picks a card without replacement, the probability of picking the second card changes, so they are dependent events.

b. • P(4 and then E): $\frac{1}{8} \times \frac{2}{7} = \frac{1}{28}$
The probability is $\frac{1}{28}$.
• P(two E's): $\frac{2}{8} \times \frac{1}{7} = \frac{1}{28}$
The probability is $\frac{1}{28}$.
• P(a vowel and then a number): $\frac{2}{8} \times \frac{4}{7} = \frac{1}{7}$
The probability is $\frac{1}{7}$.
• P(two K's): $\frac{1}{8} \times \frac{0}{7} = 0$
The probability is 0.
• P(K and then 3): $\frac{1}{8} \times \frac{2}{7} = \frac{1}{28}$
The probability is $\frac{1}{28}$.

c. $\frac{4}{8} \times \frac{3}{7} \times \frac{2}{6} = \frac{1}{14}$
The probability is $\frac{1}{14}$.

5a.

1st Ball	**2nd Ball**	**Outcome**

Green $\frac{5}{10}$ — $\frac{4}{9}$ Green — Green, Green
— $\frac{5}{9}$ Yellow — Green, Yellow
Yellow $\frac{5}{10}$ — $\frac{5}{9}$ Green — Yellow, Green
— $\frac{4}{9}$ Yellow — Yellow, Yellow

b. • P(2 Green): $\frac{5}{10} \times \frac{4}{9} = \frac{2}{9}$
The probability is $\frac{2}{9}$.
• P(1 Yellow, 1 Green):
$\frac{5}{10} \times \frac{5}{9} + \frac{5}{10} \times \frac{5}{9} = \frac{5}{18} + \frac{5}{18} = \frac{10}{18} = \frac{5}{9}$
The probability is $\frac{5}{9}$.
• P(the same colour for both):
$\frac{5}{10} \times \frac{4}{9} + \frac{5}{10} \times \frac{4}{9} = \frac{2}{9} + \frac{2}{9} = \frac{4}{9}$
The probability is $\frac{4}{9}$.

c. $\frac{5}{10} \times \frac{4}{9} \times \frac{3}{8} = \frac{1}{12}$
The probability is $\frac{1}{12}$.

6a. $\frac{8}{15} \times \frac{7}{14} = \frac{4}{15}$
The probability is $\frac{4}{15}$.

b. $\frac{8}{15} \times \frac{7}{14} + \frac{7}{15} \times \frac{8}{14} = \frac{4}{15} + \frac{4}{15} = \frac{8}{15}$
The probability is $\frac{8}{15}$.

7a. $\frac{6}{25} \times \frac{5}{24} = \frac{1}{20}$
The probability is $\frac{1}{20}$.

b. $\frac{19}{25} \times \frac{18}{24} = \frac{57}{100}$
The probability is $\frac{57}{100}$.

8a. $\frac{1}{2} \times \frac{1}{2} + \frac{1}{2} \times \frac{1}{2} = \frac{1}{4} + \frac{1}{4} = \frac{1}{2}$
The probability is $\frac{1}{2}$.

b. $\frac{1}{2} \times \frac{1}{2} = \frac{1}{4}$
The probability is $\frac{1}{4}$.

9a. • 1 red candy and 1 yellow candy:
Joshua: $\frac{10}{16} \times \frac{6}{16} + \frac{6}{16} \times \frac{10}{16} = \frac{15}{64} + \frac{15}{64} = \frac{15}{32}$
Esther: $\frac{8}{16} \times \frac{8}{15} + \frac{8}{16} \times \frac{8}{15} = \frac{4}{15} + \frac{4}{15} = \frac{8}{15}$
The probabilities are $\frac{15}{32}$ and $\frac{8}{15}$ for Joshua and Esther respectively.
• 2 yellow candies:
Joshua: $\frac{6}{16} \times \frac{6}{16} = \frac{9}{64}$
Esther: $\frac{8}{16} \times \frac{7}{15} = \frac{7}{30}$
The probabilities are $\frac{9}{64}$ and $\frac{7}{30}$ for Joshua and Esther respectively.

b. Joshua: $\frac{6}{16}$ Esther: $\frac{8}{15}$ ◄greater
Esther's probability is greater.

10a. $\frac{13}{52} \times \frac{12}{51} = \frac{1}{17}$
The probability is $\frac{1}{17}$.

ISBN: 978-1-77149-206-5

b. $\dfrac{4}{52} \times \dfrac{3}{51} = \dfrac{1}{221}$

The probability is $\dfrac{1}{221}$.

c. $\dfrac{1}{52} \times \dfrac{3}{51} = \dfrac{1}{884}$

The probability is $\dfrac{1}{884}$.

Critical-thinking Questions

Unit 1

1. $\dfrac{\$85.20}{(\$85.20 + \$482.80)} = 0.15 = 15\%$;

   $\$39.60 \div 15\% = \$264$;

   $\$264 - \$39.60 = \$224.40$;

   $\$224.40$

2. Green candies: $25 \times \dfrac{1}{5} = 5$

   Red candies: $(25 - 5) \times \dfrac{2}{5} = 8$

   Yellow candies: $25 - 5 - 8 = 12$

   Probability: $\dfrac{5}{25} \times \dfrac{12}{24} = \dfrac{1}{10}$

   The probability is $\dfrac{1}{10}$.

3. diameter:height = 2:1 = 2r:r

   $2\pi r^2 + 2\pi rh = 1256$

   $2\pi r^2 + 2\pi r^2 = 1256$ ←$h = r$

   $4\pi r^2 = 1256$

   $r^2 = 100$

   $r = 10$

   Volume: $3.14 \times 10^2 \times 10 = 3140$

   The volume of the container is 3140 cm³.

4. Length of ramp: $\sqrt{2^2 + (2^{-1})^2} = \sqrt{2 + \dfrac{1}{4}} = 1.5$

   Circumference of barrel: $1.5 \div 4 = 0.375$

   Radius: $0.375 \div 3.14 \div 2 = 0.06$ (m) $= 6$ (cm)

   The radius of the barrel is 6 cm.

5. 2:30 = 2.5 hours after 12:00

   $\dfrac{x}{360} = \dfrac{2.5}{12}$

   $12x = 900$

   $x = 75$

   By supplementary angles: $180° - 75° = 105°$

   The measure is 105°.

6. $\dfrac{30 \times 60\% + x}{30 + 20} \geq 70\%$

   $18 + x \geq 35$

   $x \geq 17$

   They must win at least 17 competitions.

7. At 4.5 s: $h = (4.5)^3 = 4.5 \times 4.5 \times 4.5 = 91.125$

   At 5 s: $h = 5^3 = 5 \times 5 \times 5 = 125$

   Difference: $125 - 91.125 = 33.875$

   The difference in height is 33.875 m.

8. Height of triangle: $\sqrt{8^2 - (8 \div 2)^2} = 6.93$

   Surface area:

   $8 \times 6.93 \div 2 \times 2 + 8 \times 15 \times 3 = 415.44$

   The surface area is 415.44 cm².

9.

Time (min)	Distance (m)
1	11)+8
2	19)+8
3	27

Equation: $d = 8t + 3$

After 10 min: $d = 8 \times 10 + 3 = 83$

Yes, he will have walked 80 m after 10 min.

10. Turtle Sandra's speed: $30 \div 2.5 = 12$

    $12t - 25 = 8t + 3$

    $4t = 28$

    $t = 7$

    It will take Turtle Sandra 7 min to catch up.

11. Bottom of ski lift: (1,-1)

    Slope: $\dfrac{2 - (-1)}{-3 - 1} = -\dfrac{3}{4}$

    The slope is $-\dfrac{3}{4}$.

12. Length of 1 unit: $0.2 \div 2 = 0.1$

    Length of ski lift in units: $\sqrt{3^2 + 4^2} = 5$

    Length of ski lift in km: $0.1 \times 5 = 0.5$

    The length of the ski lift is 0.5 km.

13. $\overline{AC}$: $\sqrt{12^2 + 16^2} = 20$

    $\overline{CE}$: $20 - 8 = 12$

    By alternate angles: $\angle ACB = \angle DEC$

    By ASA: $\angle ACB = \angle DEC$

    $\overline{BC} = \overline{CE} = 12$ cm

    $\angle ABC = \angle DCE = 90°$

    $\triangle ABC \cong \triangle DCE$

    Yes, $\triangle ABC$ and $\triangle DCE$ are congruent.

14. green:red = 8:3 = 16:6

    blue:red = 1:2 = 3:6

    green:red:blue = 16:6:3 = 32:12:6

    Total marbles: $32 + 12 + 6 = 50$

    Probability: $\dfrac{6}{50} \times \dfrac{5}{49} = \dfrac{3}{245}$

    The probability is $\dfrac{3}{245}$.

15. $78.5 < \pi r^2 < 113.04$

    $78.5 < \pi r^2$ $\pi r^2 < 113.04$

    $25 < r^2$ $r^2 < 36$

    $5 < r$ $r < 6$

    $5 < r < 6$

    $2 \times 3.14 \times 5 < 2\pi r < 2 \times 3.14 \times 6$

    $31.4 < 2\pi r < 37.68$

    It is between 31.4 cm and 37.68 cm.

ISBN: 978-1-77149-206-5

▪ Answers ··

16. **May**

x	y
1	7
8	0

Dawn

x	y
1	0
8	14

May's and Dawn's Savings

Dawn's savings in Week 7: $12
May's savings in Week 7: $1
Difference: $12 – $1 = $11
Dawn had $11 more than May in Week 7.

17.

Week	Savings ($)
2	6
4	8
6	10
8	12

Equation: $y = x + 4$
In Week 8, Serena had $12.

18. Let s be the side length of the cube.
Height of cylinder: s
Radius of cylinder: $\frac{s}{2}$

Percent cut out: $\frac{\pi r^2 h}{s^3} \times 100\%$

$$= \frac{\pi(\frac{s}{2})^2 \times s}{s^3} \times 100\%$$

$$= \frac{\pi \times \frac{s^2}{4} \times s}{s^3} \times 100\%$$

$$= \frac{3.14}{4} \times 100\%$$

$$= 78.5\%$$

78.5% of the cube is cut out.

19. Jason's speed: $15 \div 25 = \frac{3}{5}$ (potatoes/min)

Janette's speed: $\frac{1}{10}$ h = 6 min

$8 \div 6 = \frac{4}{3}$ (potatoes/min)

Combined speed: $\frac{3}{5} + \frac{4}{3} = 1\frac{14}{15}$

Time needed: $406 \div 1\frac{14}{15} = 210$

It will take them 210 min.

20. Side length of base: $\sqrt{100} = 10$
Height of triangle: $\sqrt{12^2 + (10 \div 2)^2} = 13$
Surface area: $100 + 10 \times 13 \div 2 \times 4 = 360$
Volume: $\frac{1}{3} \times 10 \times 10 \times 12 = 400$
The surface area is 360 cm² and the volume is 400 cm³.

Unit 2

1. $\frac{1}{3} \times 3.14 \times 9^2 \times 12.5 = 1059.75$;
$1059.75 \div 7.5 \div 6 = 23.55$; 23.55 cm

2. Radius of each circle: $28.26 \div 3.14 \div 2 = 4.5$
Side length of triangle: $4.5 \times 2 = 9$
Height of triangle: $\sqrt{9^2 - 4.5^2} = 7.79$
Area of triangle: $9 \times 7.79 \div 2 = 35.055$
The area is 35.055 cm².

3. Games won: $20 - 20 \times 15\% = 17$

$$\frac{17 + x}{20 + 16} \geq 75\%$$

$$17 + x \geq 27$$

$$x \geq 10$$

They need to win at least 10 games.

4. Truck: $4.65 \div 40\frac{1}{10} = 0.116$ (L/km)

Van: $4\frac{1}{2} \div 40 = 0.1125$ (L/km)

The van is more gas efficient.

5. Volume of 1 cube: $3.84 \times 10^5 \div 6 = 64\,000$
Side length: $s^3 = 64\,000$
$$s = 40$$
The side length is 40 cm.

6. large radius:small radius $= 3:1 = 3r:r$
Shaded area: $\pi(3r)^2 - \pi r^2 = 9\pi r^2 - \pi r^2 = 8\pi r^2$
Total area: $\pi(3r)^2 = 9\pi r^2$
P(hitting shaded area): $\frac{8\pi r^2}{9\pi r^2} = \frac{8}{9}$

P(twice in a row): $\frac{8}{9} \times \frac{8}{9} = \frac{64}{81}$

The probability is $\frac{64}{81}$.

7. $3.14 \times 8 \times s + 3.14 \times 8^2 = 628$
$$25.12s + 200.96 = 628$$
$$25.12s = 427.04$$
$$s = 17$$

Height: $\sqrt{17^2 - 8^2} = 15$

Volume: $\frac{1}{3} \times 3.14 \times 8^2 \times 15 = 1004.8$

Its volume is 1004.8 cm³.

8. $\overline{AC} = 5 \times 2 = 10$

$$\frac{DE}{AB} = \frac{DC}{AC}$$

$$\frac{DE}{12} = \frac{5}{10}$$

$$DE = 6$$

$\overline{BC}: \sqrt{12^2 - 10^2} = 6.63$ $\overline{EC}: \sqrt{6^2 - 5^2} = 3.32$
Perimeter of $\triangle ABC$: $12 + 10 + 6.63 = 28.63$
Perimeter of $\triangle DEC$: $6 + 5 + 3.32 = 14.32$
The perimeters of $\triangle ABC$ and $\triangle DEC$ are 28.63 cm and 14.32 cm respectively.

9. $\frac{2n^2}{4n^4} \times \frac{2n^2 - 1}{4n^4 - 1} = \frac{1}{2n^2} \times \frac{2n^2 - 1}{4n^4 - 1} = \frac{2n^2 - 1}{8n^6 - 2n^2}$
The probability is $\frac{2n^2 - 1}{8n^6 - 2n^2}$.

10. Old surface area: $4 \times 3.14 \times 8^2 = 803.84$
New surface area: $4 \times 3.14 \times 10^2 = 1256$

Increase: $\frac{1256 - 803.84}{803.84} \times 100\% = 56.25\%$

The surface area increased by 56.25%.

ISBN: 978-1-77149-206-5

11.

x-coordinate	y-coordinate
0	1
1	2
2	3
3	4

Equation: $y = x + 1$

12.

x-coordinate	y-coordinate
-2	-1
-1	-2
0	-3
1	-4

Equation: $y = -x - 3$

They intersect at (-2,-1).

13. large radius:small radius = 2:1 = 4:2
Volume of small cylinder: $3.14 \times 2^2 \times 2 = 25.12$
Volume of large cylinder: $3.14 \times 4^2 \times 2 = 100.48$
Surface area of small cylinder:
$2 \times 3.14 \times 2^2 + 2 \times 3.14 \times 2 \times 2 = 50.24$
Surface area of large cylinder:
$2 \times 3.14 \times 4^2 + 2 \times 3.14 \times 4 \times 2 = 150.72$
Volume ratio: 100.48:25.12 = 4:1
Surface area: 150.72:50.24 = 3:1
The ratios are 4:1 for their volumes and 3:1 for their surface areas.

14. Income tax: $\$54\,000 \times \frac{5}{6} \times 15\% + (\$54\,000$
$- (\$54\,000 \times \frac{5}{6})) \times 20\% = \$8550$
Money after tax: $\$54\,000 - \$8550 = \$45\,450$
Arnold made $45 450 after tax last year.

15. Let b be the base of the first right triangle.
$b \times b \div 2 = (b - 3)(4b) \div 2$
$b^2 = 4b^2 - 12b$
$12b = 3b^2$
$12 = 3b$
$b = 4$

Hypotenuse:
$\sqrt{4^2 + 4^2} = 5.66$
Perimeter:
$4 + 4 + 5.66 = 13.66$

Hypotenuse:
$\sqrt{16^2 + 1^2} = 16.03$
Perimeter:
$16 + 1 + 16.03 = 33.03$

Difference: $33.03 - 13.66 = 19.37$
The difference is 19.37 cm.

16. $(\sqrt{x} - 5)^3 \geq 64$
$\sqrt{x} - 5 \geq 4$
$\sqrt{x} \geq 9$
$x \geq 81$ It was at least 81 cm².

17. Radius: $6 \div 2 = 3$
$\frac{4}{3} \times 3.14 \times 3^3 \div 2 + \frac{1}{3} \times 3.14 \times 3^2 \times h = 150.72$
$56.52 + 9.42h = 150.72$
$9.42h = 94.2$
$h = 10$

Total height: $3 + 10 = 13$
The total height of the toy is 13 cm.

18. Height of base: $\sqrt{5.8^2 - (5.8 \div 2)^2} = 5.02$
Surface area:
$5.8 \times 5.02 \div 2 \times 2 + 5.8 \times 20 \times 3 = 377.116$
The surface area is 377.116 cm².

19. Amy's rate: $1\frac{3}{4}$ h ÷ 5 chairs = 0.35 h/chair
Ben's rate: $1\frac{2}{5}$ h ÷ 7 chairs = 0.2 h/chair
Difference in h/chair: $0.35 - 0.2 = 0.15$
Difference in hours: $0.15 \times 3 = 0.45$
It is 0.15 h/chair and is 0.45 h for 3 chairs.

20. By consecutive interior angles:
$\angle BDE + \angle AED = 180°$
$\frac{46x + 28}{0.4x} + \frac{16x - 3}{0.4x} = 180$
$\frac{62x + 25}{0.4x} \times 0.4x = 180 \times 0.4x$
$62x + 25 = 72x$
$x = 2.5$
By corresponding angles:
$\angle AED = \angle BDC = \frac{16(2.5) - 3}{0.4(2.5)} = 37°$
$\angle BDC = \angle DBC = 37°$ (isosceles triangle)
By angles in a triangle:
$\angle BCD + 37° + 37° = 180°$
$\angle BCD = 106°$
$\angle BCD$ is 106°.

Unit 3

1. $3.14 \times 3^2 \times 8 = 226.08$;
$3.14 \times 4^2 \times 9 = 452.16$;
$226.08 \div 452.16 \times 100\% = 50\%$; 50%

2. P(red ball) = $\frac{1}{5}$
If the first ball was replaced:
P(2 red balls) = $\frac{1}{5} \times \frac{1}{5} = \frac{1}{25} = 4\%$
Since the probability was less than 4%, the first ball was not replaced before she picked the second ball.

3. $(\frac{1}{2})^{-2} = (2^{-1})^{-2} = 4$
$\overline{BE}: \sqrt{2^2 + \sqrt{3}^2} = \sqrt{7}$ $\overline{CE}: \sqrt{4^2 - \sqrt{5}^2} = \sqrt{11}$
$\overline{BC}: \sqrt{\sqrt{11}^2 - \sqrt{7}^2} = \sqrt{4} = 2$
Area:
$2 \times \sqrt{3} \div 2 + \sqrt{7} \times 2 \div 2 + \sqrt{5} \times \sqrt{11} \div 2 = 8.09$
Perimeter: $2 + 2 + 4 + \sqrt{5} + \sqrt{3} = 11.97$
The area is 8.09 cm² and the perimeter is 11.97 cm.

4. Percent increased:
$\frac{\$7.83 - \$6.75}{\$6.75} \times 100\% = 16\%$
Original price:
$\$18.85 \div (1 + 16\%) = \$16.25$
The original price was $16.25.

ISBN: 978-1-77149-206-5

5. Area of entire circle: $3.14 \times 6^2 = 113.04$

$\dfrac{a}{360} = \dfrac{(113.04 - 94.2)}{113.04}$

$113.04a = 6782.4$

$a = 60$

a is 60°.

6. Surface area:

$2 \times 3.14 \times 10^2 + 2 \times 3.14 \times 10 \times 8 = 1130.4$

Time for 1 coat: $1130.4 \div 1.875 = 602.88$

Time for 3 coats: $602.88 \times 3 = 1808.64$

Time in minutes: $1808.64 \div 60 = 30.144$

It will take her 30.144 minutes.

7. Possible triangles:

congruent by SAS   not congruent

not congruent

The probability is $\dfrac{1}{3}$.

8. $\dfrac{2x^3}{4x^2} = \dfrac{2x^3 + 8x}{80}$

$\dfrac{x}{2} = \dfrac{2x^3 + 8x}{80}$

$80x = 4x^3 + 16x$

$64x = 4x^3$

$64 = 4x^2$

$16 = x^2$

$4 = x$

Speed: $\dfrac{2(4)^3}{4(4)^2} = \dfrac{128}{64} = 2$

John's speed was 2 m/s.

9. $3.14 \times 6 \times s + 3.14 \times 6^2 = 301.44$

$\quad 18.84s + 113.04 = 301.44$

$\quad\quad\quad 18.84s = 188.4$

$\quad\quad\quad\quad\quad s = 10$

Height of cone: $\sqrt{10^2 - 6^2} = 8$

Surface area of half cone:

$301.44 \div 2 + (6 \times 2) \times 8 \div 2 = 198.72$

The surface area of each half is 198.72 cm².

10. $3a \times 2a \times 5a = 3750$ Length: $3 \times 5 = 15$

$\quad\quad\quad 30a^3 = 3750$ Height: $5 \times 5 = 25$

$\quad\quad\quad\quad a^3 = 125$ Width: $2 \times 5 = 10$

$\quad\quad\quad\quad\quad a = 5$

Surface area:

$15 \times 10 \times 2 + 15 \times 25 \times 2 + 10 \times 25 \times 2 = 1550$

Its surface area is 1550 cm².

11. By corresponding angles: $\angle BAC = \angle DCE$

$\quad\quad\quad\quad\quad\quad\quad\quad\quad\quad \angle BCA = \angle DEC$

By angles in a triangle:

$\angle BAC + \angle BCA + \angle ABC = 180°$

$\angle ABC = 180° - \angle BAC - \angle BCA$

$\quad\quad\quad = 180° - \angle DCE - \angle DEC$

$\quad\quad\quad = \angle CDE$

$\triangle ABC$ and $\triangle CDE$ are similar.

$\dfrac{AB}{7.5} = \dfrac{4}{10}$

$10 \times AB = 30$

$\quad\quad AB = 3$

The length of $\overline{AB}$ is 3 cm.

12. Let s be the side length of each square.

$s^2 + s^2 = 5^2$

$\quad 2s^2 = 25$

$\quad\quad s = \sqrt{12.5}$

Area of 1 square: $\sqrt{12.5}^{\,2} = 12.5$

Area of circle: $3.14 \times 5^2 = 78.5$

Area not covered: $78.5 - 12.5 \times 2 = 53.5$

The area is 53.5 cm².

13. Area covered in 1 rotation:

$2 \times 3.14 \times 3 \times 10 = 188.4$

No. of rotations: $30\,000 \div 188.4 = 159.24$

Rate: $159.24 \div 4 = 39.81$

The rate is 39.81 rotations/min.

14. $y = -\dfrac{1}{2}x + 2$ $y = -2x - 1$ $y = x - 1$

x	y
-2	3
0	2
2	1

x	y
-1	1
0	-1
1	-3

x	y
-2	-3
0	-1
2	1

They are (-2,3), (0,-1), and (2,1).

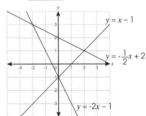

15. Distance between (-2,3) and (0,-1):

$\sqrt{2^2 + 4^2} \times 5 = 22.36$

Distance between (-2,3) and (2,1):

$\sqrt{4^2 + 2^2} \times 5 = 22.36$

Distance between (0,-1) and (2,1):

$\sqrt{2^2 + 2^2} \times 5 = 14.14$

Perimeter: $22.36 + 22.36 + 14.14 = 58.86$

The perimeter is 58.86 m.

16. Let x be the last integer.

Possible equations:

- $x^2 + 9^2 = 3^2 + 7^2$

$x^2 + 81 = 58$

$\quad\quad x = \sqrt{-23}$ ← not an integer

- $x^2 + 7^2 = 3^2 + 9^2$

$x^2 + 49 = 90$

$\quad\quad x = \sqrt{41}$ ← not an integer

- $x^2 + 3^2 = 7^2 + 9^2$

$x^2 + 9 = 130$

$\quad\quad x^2 = 121$

$\quad\quad\quad x = 11$ ← integer

The last integer is 11.

ISBN: 978-1-77149-206-5

17. $1\frac{3}{4} \div 3\frac{1}{3} \times 100\% = \frac{7}{4} \times \frac{3}{10} \times 100\% = 52.5\%$

52.5% of the juice is consumed.

18. $7 \ge x - 4$ $x + (-25) \ge -17$

$11 \ge x$ $x \ge 8$

$\qquad\qquad 11 \ge x \ge 8$

Possible integers: 8, 9, 10, 11

Probability: $\frac{1}{4}$ └ divisible by 3

The probability is $\frac{1}{4}$.

19. Circumference: $12.56 + 6.28 = 18.84$

Radius: $18.84 \div 3.14 \div 2 = 3$

$\overline{AB} = \overline{BC} = 3$

$$\frac{\angle ABC}{360} = \frac{6.28}{18.84}$$

$18.84 \times \angle ABC = 2260.8$

$\angle ABC = 120$

By angles in a triangle:

$\angle DEF + 30° + 30° = 180°$

$\qquad\qquad\quad \angle DEF = 120°$

$\overline{AB} = \overline{DE} = 3$ cm

$\angle ABC = \angle DEF = 120°$

$\overline{BC} = \overline{EF} = 3$ cm

$\triangle ABC \cong \triangle DEF$ by SAS

Yes, $\triangle ABC$ and $\triangle DEF$ are congruent.

20. The side length of the cube (s) equals the diameter of the sphere ($2r$).

$$s^3 - \frac{4}{3}\pi r^3 = 822\frac{6}{7}$$

$$(2r)^3 - \frac{4}{3} \times \frac{22}{7} \times r^3 = 822\frac{6}{7}$$

$$8r^3 - 4\frac{4}{21} \times r^3 = 822\frac{6}{7}$$

$$3\frac{17}{21} \times r^3 = 822\frac{6}{7}$$

$$r^3 = 216$$

$$r = 6$$

Surface area of sphere: $4 \times \frac{22}{7} \times 6^2 = 452\frac{4}{7}$

The surface area is $452\frac{4}{7}$ cm².

Unit 4

1. $\sqrt{77^2 + 36^2} = 85$; $85 \div 1.7 = 50$; 50 s

2. Translation: x-coordinate: $-1\frac{1}{2} + 2\frac{1}{2} = 1$

$\qquad\qquad\quad$ y-coordinate: $6\frac{1}{2} - 9\frac{1}{2} = -3$

Reflection: (1,-3) to (-1,-3)

Slope: $\dfrac{6\frac{1}{2} - (-3)}{-1\frac{1}{2} - (-1)} = \dfrac{9\frac{1}{2}}{-\frac{1}{2}} = -19$

The slope of $\overline{ST}$ is -19.

3. Let w be the number of weeks.

$(20 - 4.25) \times w \ge 18.9 \times 5$

$\qquad 15.75w \ge 94.5$

$\qquad\qquad w \ge 6$

Frederick needs at least 6 weeks.

4. Side length of square: $\sqrt{20.5}$

Area of circle: $3.14 \times \sqrt{20.5}^{\,2} = 64.37$

The area of the circle is 64.37 cm².

5. Let r be the number of red cards.

$$\frac{r}{5} \times \frac{r}{5} = \frac{4}{25}$$

$$\frac{r^2}{25} = \frac{4}{25}$$

$$r^2 = 4$$

$$r = 2$$

There are 2 red cards.

6. Side length of cube: $s^3 = 216$

$\qquad\qquad\qquad\qquad\quad s = 6$

Let h be the height of the pyramid.

$\frac{1}{3} \times 6^2 \times h = 216$

$\qquad\qquad h = 18$

Difference: $18 - 6 = 12$

The pyramid is 12 cm taller.

7. By corresponding angles and supplementary angles:

$6x + 8 + x + 7.5 = 180$

$\qquad\quad 7x = 164.5$

$\qquad\quad\; x = 23.5$

By opposite angles: $3y - 1 = 6x + 8$

$\qquad\qquad\qquad\qquad 3y = 6(23.5) + 8 + 1$

$\qquad\qquad\qquad\qquad 3y = 150$

$\qquad\qquad\qquad\qquad\; y = 50$

Ratio: $x:y = 23.5:50 = 47:100$

The ratio is 47:100.

8. Surface area of cylinder:

$2 \times 3.14 \times 6^2 + 2 \times 3.14 \times 6 \times 8 = 527.52$

Side of cone: $\sqrt{6^2 + 8^2} = 10$

Surface area of cone:

$3.14 \times 6 \times 10 + 3.14 \times 6^2 = 301.44$

Difference: $527.52 - 301.44 = 226.08$ cm².

The change is 226.08 cm².

9. $\dfrac{AB}{DE} = \dfrac{BC}{EF}$ $\dfrac{AC}{DF} = \dfrac{BC}{EF}$

$\dfrac{8.4}{DE} = \dfrac{15}{10}$ $\dfrac{12.75}{DF} = \dfrac{15}{10}$

$DE = 5.6$ $DF = 8.5$

By angles in a triangle:

$\angle BAC + 58° + 34° = 180°$

$\qquad\qquad \angle BAC = 88°$

$\angle EDF = \angle BAC = 88°$ (by similar triangles)

$\overline{DE} = \overline{IH} = 5.6$ cm

$\angle EDF = \angle HIG = 88°$

$\overline{DF} = \overline{IG} = 8.5$ cm

$\triangle DEF \cong \triangle IHG$ by SAS

Yes, $\triangle DEF$ and $\triangle IHG$ are congruent.

10. Height at 1.4 s: $6 \times 1.4 - 1.4^2 = 6.44$

Height at 4.7 s: $6 \times 4.7 - 4.7^2 = 6.11$

The ball was higher at 1.4 s.

11. Radius: $8 \div 2 = 4$ (mm) = 0.4 (cm)

    Volume: $\frac{4}{3} \times 3.14 \times 0.4^3 \div 2 + 3.14 \times 0.4^2 \times 8.7 + \frac{1}{3} \times 3.14 \times 0.4^2 \times 1.3 = 4.72$

    Surface area: $4 \times 3.14 \times 0.4^2 \div 2 + 2 \times 3.14 \times 0.4 \times 8.7 + 3.14 \times 0.4 \times 1.36 = 24.57$

    The volume is 4.72 cm³ and the surface area is 24.57 cm².

12. Volume decreased: $4.72 \times 20\% = 0.944$

    Height decreased: $0.944 \div (3.14 \times 0.4^2) = 1.88$

    Length now: $0.4 + 8.7 + 1.3 - 1.88 = 8.52$

    The pencil will be 8.52 cm long.

13. Probability of losses: $1 - 0.1 - 0.3 = 0.6$

	Win (0.1)	Draw (0.3)	Loss (0.6)
Win (0.1)	$0.1 \times 0.1 = 0.01$	$0.3 \times 0.1 = 0.03$	$0.6 \times 0.1 = 0.06$
Draw (0.3)	$0.1 \times 0.3 = 0.03$	$0.3 \times 0.3 = 0.09$	$0.6 \times 0.3 = 0.18$
Loss (0.6)	$0.1 \times 0.6 = 0.06$	$0.3 \times 0.6 = 0.18$	$0.6 \times 0.6 = 0.36$

    P(at least 1 win):

    $0.01 + 0.03 + 0.06 + 0.03 + 0.06 = 0.19$

    The probability is 0.19.

14. $2 \times 3.14 \times r > 47.1$

    $r > 7.5$

    $r^2 > 56.25$

    $\pi r^2 > 176.625$

    It is greater than 176.625 cm².

15. Amount spilled: $3\frac{1}{3} \times 45\% = 1\frac{1}{2}$

    Amount remaining: $3\frac{1}{3} - 1\frac{1}{2} = 1\frac{5}{6}$

    $1\frac{5}{6}$ L of apple cider remains.

16. $-1\frac{1}{2} = \frac{4-y}{-3-3}$

    $9 = 4 - y$

    $y = -5$

    Mavis's y-coordinate is -5.

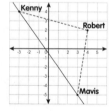

17. Units between Kenny and Mavis:

    $\sqrt{9^2 + 6^2} = 10.82$

    Distance of 1 unit: $541 \div 10.82 = 50$

    Distance between Kenny and Robert:

    $\sqrt{7^2 + 2^2} \times 50 = 364.01$

    Distance between Mavis and Robert:

    $\sqrt{7^2 + 1^2} \times 50 = 353.55$

    Difference: $364.01 - 353.55 = 10.46$

    Mavis lives closer to Robert by 10.46 m.

18. Volume of ball: $\frac{4}{3} \times 3.14 \times 3^3 = 113.04$

    Base of cylinder: $3.14 \times (10 \div 2)^2 = 78.5$

    Height increased: $113.04 \div 78.5 = 1.44$

    It will rise by 1.44 cm.

19. Let c be the weight of the cheesecake.

    $$2\frac{1}{10} + c(1 - \frac{1}{4}) < 4\frac{1}{2}$$
    $$2\frac{1}{10} + \frac{3}{4}c < 4\frac{1}{2}$$
    $$\frac{3}{4}c < 2\frac{2}{5}$$
    $$c < 3\frac{1}{5}$$

    The cheesecake weighed less than $3\frac{1}{5}$ kg.

20. people:doctor = $\overset{\times 40}{\overbrace{3000:7}} = 1.2 \times 10^5:\underset{\times 40}{\underbrace{280}}$

    There are 280 doctors in the town.

Unit 5

1. $\$1029 \times (1 - 15\%) = \$874.65$;

    $\$874.65 - \$34.25 = \$840.40$;

    $\$840.40 \div (1 - 12\%) = \$955$; $\$955$

2. Height of triangle:

    $$\sqrt{s^2 - (\tfrac{s}{2})^2} = \sqrt{s^2 - \tfrac{s^2}{4}} = \sqrt{\tfrac{3}{4}s^2} = \frac{\sqrt{3}}{2}s$$

    Area: $s \times \frac{\sqrt{3}}{2}s \div 2 = \frac{\sqrt{3}}{4}s^2$

    The area of an equilateral triangle is $\frac{\sqrt{3}}{4}s^2$.

3. Radius: $8 \div 2 = 4$

    Height of triangle: $\sqrt{4^2 - (4 \div 2)^2} = \sqrt{12}$

    Area of triangle: $\sqrt{12} \times 4 \div 2 = 6.93$

    Area of hexagon: $6.93 \times 6 = 41.58$

    Area of circle: $3.14 \times 4^2 = 50.24$

    Shaded area: $50.24 - 41.58 = 8.66$

    The area of the shaded part is 8.66 cm².

4. No. of adults: $400 \times 85.75\% = 343$

    No. of children: $400 - 343 = 57$

    Probability: $\frac{57}{400} \times \frac{56}{399} = \frac{1}{50}$

    The probability is $\frac{1}{50}$.

5. By angles in a triangle:

    $$2\frac{1}{3}x^3 + 30 + 2x^3 - 3 + 1\frac{1}{3}x^3 = 180$$
    $$5\frac{2}{3}x^3 = 153$$
    $$x^3 = 27$$
    $$x = 3$$

    The value of x is 3.

6. Capacity: $3.14 \times (9 \div 2)^2 \times 16 = 1017.36$

    Water in glass: $1017.36 \times \frac{2}{3} = 678.24$

    Water that can be added:

    $1017.36 - 678.24 = 339.12$ (cm³) = 339.12 (mL)

    339.12 mL of water can be added.

ISBN: 978-1-77149-206-5

7. Radius: $10 \div 2 = 5$
Surface area before: $4 \times 3.14 \times 5^2 = 314$
Surface area after: $314 \times (1 + 44\%) = 452.16$
$4\pi r^2 = 452.16$
$\quad r^2 = 36$
$\quad r = 6$
New diameter: $6 \times 2 = 12$
The diameter is 12 cm.

8. By corresponding angles: $\angle CAB = \angle ECD$
$\angle BCA = \angle DEC$
$\angle ABC = \angle CDE$
$\triangle ABC$ and $\triangle CDE$ are similar triangles.
Ratio: $4:6 = 2:3$
$\quad x:5 = 2:3$, so $x = 3\frac{1}{3}$
$\quad 3:y = 2:3$, so $y = 4\frac{1}{2}$
The ratio is 2:3. The value of x is $3\frac{1}{3}$ and the value of y is $4\frac{1}{2}$.

9. $3.14 \times r^2 \div 2 > 0.98$
$\quad r^2 > 0.62$
$\quad r > 0.79$
$2r > 0.79 \times 2$
$d > 1.58$
The diameter is greater than 1.58 m.

10. P(drawing a non-winning ball first):
$\dfrac{8-3}{8} = \dfrac{5}{8}$
Let p be the probability of drawing two non-winning balls.
$\dfrac{5}{8} \times p = \dfrac{5}{14}$
$\quad p = \dfrac{4}{7}$
Ratio: 4:7
The ratio is 4:7.

11. $\overline{AB} = 3 \qquad\qquad \overline{AC} = 4$
$\overline{BC} = \sqrt{3^2 + 4^2} = 5$
$\overline{DE} = \sqrt{(0.8-(-1))^2 + ((-1.6)-(-4))^2} = 3$
$\overline{DF} = \sqrt{(4-0.8)^2 + ((-1.6)-(-4))^2} = 4$
$\overline{EF} = 5$
$\overline{AB} = \overline{DE} \qquad \overline{AC} = \overline{DF} \qquad \overline{BC} = \overline{EF}$
$\triangle ABC \cong \triangle DEF$ by SSS
$\triangle ABC$ and $\triangle DEF$ are congruent.

12. Slope of $\overline{BC} = \dfrac{5-1}{-1-(-4)} = \dfrac{4}{3}$

x	y
-3	-4
0	0
3	4

Equation: $y = \dfrac{4}{3}x$

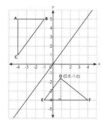

13. Radius: $1.3 \times 10^4 \div 2 = 6.5 \times 10^3$
Volume: $\dfrac{4}{3} \times 3.14 \times (6.5 \times 10^3)^3$
$\qquad = 1.15 \times 10^{12}$
Surface area: $4 \times 3.14 \times (6.5 \times 10^3)^2$
$\qquad\qquad = 5.31 \times 10^8$
Its volume would be 1.15×10^{12} km³ and its surface area would be 5.31×10^8 km².

14. Let t be the time taken to reach each other.
$6.2t + 4.3t = 525$
$\qquad\quad t = 50$
Carol's distance: $6.2 \times 50 = 310$
Theresa's distance: $4.3 \times 50 = 215$
Difference: $310 - 215 = 95$
Carol will have run 95 m farther.

15. Side lengths of triangle:
$\sqrt{1^2 + 4^2} = \sqrt{17} \qquad \sqrt{4^2 + 1^2} = \sqrt{17}$
$\sqrt{3^2 + 3^2} = \sqrt{18}$
The shape is not an equilateral triangle.
Area of square: $4^2 = 16$
Area not covered by shape:
$1 \times 4 \div 2 + 4 \times 1 \div 2 + 3 \times 3 \div 2 = 8.5$
Area of shape: $16 - 8.5 = 7.5$
Fraction: $\dfrac{7.5}{16} = \dfrac{15}{32}$
It takes up $\dfrac{15}{32}$ of the square's area.

16.
x	y
1	-5
-1	-3
-2	-2
-3	-1

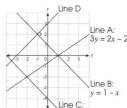

Line A: $3y = 2x - 2$
Line B: $y = 1 - x$
Line C: $y = -x - 4$

Equation: $y = -x - 4$

17. Slope: $\dfrac{3-2}{0-(-1)} = \dfrac{1}{1} = 1$
The slope of Line D is 1.

18. Radius of A: $25.12 \div 3.14 \div 2 = 4$
Radius of B: $31.4 \div 3.14 \div 2 = 5$
Radius of C: $15.7 \div 3.14 \div 2 = 2.5$
Length of $\overline{AB}$: $4 + 5 = 9$
Length of $\overline{BC}$: $5 + 2.5 = 7.5$
Length of $\overline{AC}$: $\sqrt{9^2 + 7.5^2} = 11.72$
The distance between Points A and C is 11.72 cm.

19. Let r be the sales price of each ticket.
$(625 \times (1 - 16\%))r \geq 2500 + 125$
$\qquad\qquad 525r \geq 2625$
$\qquad\qquad\quad r \geq 5$
The sales price should be at least $5/ticket.

20. Height of 1 cone: $8.6 \div 2 = 4.3$
Radius: $3.7 \div 2 = 1.85$
Side of 1 cone: $\sqrt{1.85^2 + 4.3^2} = 4.68$
Surface area: $3.14 \times 1.85 \times 4.68 \times 2 = 54.37$
54.37 cm² needs to be painted.

ISBN: 978-1-77149-206-5

Answers

Unit 6

1. Acute angle:
$$\frac{8.5}{12} \times 360° - \frac{30}{60} \times 360° = 75°$$
Reflex angle: $360° - 75° = 285°$
Ratio: $75°:285° = 5:19$
The ratio is 5:19.

2. $3x = 90°$
$x = 30°$
Angle of red section: $1\frac{1}{2} \times 30° = 45°$
Angle of green section: $180° - 90° - 30° = 60°$
$P(\text{red}) = \frac{45°}{360°} = \frac{1}{8}$ $P(\text{green}) = \frac{60°}{360°} = \frac{1}{6}$
$P(\text{red, green}) = \frac{1}{8} \times \frac{1}{6} = \frac{1}{48}$
The probability is $\frac{1}{48}$.

3. Raised price:
$593.20 \times (1 + 105\%) = \$1216.06$
Discounted price:
$\$1216.06 \times (1 - 15\%) = \$1033.65$
After tax:
$\$1033.65 \times (1 + 13\%) = \$1168.02$
The watch is $1168.02.

4. $125\,000\,000 \text{ cm}^3 = 125 \text{ m}^3$
Side length of new cube: $s^3 = 125$
$s = 5$
Original side length: $5 \div (1 + 25\%) = 4$
Surface area: $4^2 \times 6 = 96$
The surface area was 96 m².

5. An obtuse triangle has an obtuse angle and 2 acute angles.
If the angle is obtuse: $180 > 2x + 6 > 90$

$180 > 2x + 6$	$2x + 6 > 90$
$174 > 2x$	$2x > 84$
$87 > x$	$x > 42$

$87 > x > 42$
If the angle is acute: $2x + 6 < 90$
$2x < 84$
$x < 42$
The value of x can be between 42 and 87, or it can be less than 42.

6. Distance from Clara's house to the airport:
$\sqrt{8^2 + 34^2} = 34.93$
Total distance: $8 + 34.93 + 34 = 76.93$
Time: $76.93 \div 60 = 1.28$
She travelled 76.93 km. It took 1.28 hours.

7. Volume of cylinder: $\pi r^2 h$
Volume of cone: $\frac{1}{3}\pi(2r)^2 h = \frac{4}{3}\pi r^2 h$
Ratio: $\pi r^2 h : \frac{4}{3}\pi r^2 h = 1:\frac{4}{3} = 3:4 = 67.5:90$
The ratio is 3:4. The volume is 67.5 cm³.

8. Side length of square: $\sqrt{144} = 12$
Radius: $2:\sqrt{2} = 12:6\sqrt{2}$
Area of circle: $3.14 \times (6\sqrt{2})^2 = 226.08$
The area of the circle is 226.08 cm².

9. x-coordinate: $-3.5 + 2.5 = -1$
y-coordinate: $-5.5 + 5 = -0.5$
The coordinates of the new point are (-1,-0.5).
Yes, he is correct. The slope is positive because the line extends up and to the right.

10. Area of base of prism: $720 \div 15 = 48$
(Suggested answers)
Possible quadrilaterals with no right angles:

It could be a parallelogram with a base of 8 cm and a height of 6 cm or a trapezoid with bases of 6 cm and 10 cm, and a height of 6 cm.

11. Surface area: $4 \times 3.14 \times 3^2 = 113.04$
Paint used: $\frac{x}{113.04} = \frac{0.156}{1}$
$x = 17.63$
Arnold used 17.63 mL of paint.

12. red to blue = 3:4 = 6:8
green to red = 1:6
green to red to blue = 1:6:8
Probability: $\frac{1}{1+8} = \frac{1}{9}$
The probability is $\frac{1}{9}$.

13. $\frac{8t^2(t + 3^2)}{2^3\sqrt{t^2}} = \frac{8t^2(t + 9)}{8t} = t(t + 9) = t^2 + 9t$
Jon: $(9\frac{1}{2})^2 + 9(9\frac{1}{2}) = 175\frac{3}{4}$
Yes, Jon and Lynn travel the same distance. Jon travels $175\frac{3}{4}$ m in $9\frac{1}{2}$ minutes.

14. Let e be the number of Eddie's marbles.
$e + 2e + \frac{1}{4}(2e) > 50$
$3\frac{1}{2}e > 50$
$e > 14\frac{2}{7}$
The minimum number of marbles that Eddie used was 15.

15. Leslie's time per lap: $210 \div 5 = 42$
Zack's time per lap: $210 \div 3.5 = 60$
LCM of 42 and 60: 420
420 s = 7 min
Meeting time: 8:00 p.m. + 7 min = 8:07 p.m.
They will meet at the starting point at 8:07 p.m.

ISBN: 978-1-77149-206-5

16. Distance:
$\sqrt{6^2 + 8^2} \times 50 = 500$
Slope:
$\frac{4 - (-4)}{3 - (-3)} = \frac{8}{6} = 1\frac{1}{3}$
Thea travelled 500 m. The
slope of the hill is $1\frac{1}{3}$.

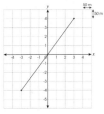

17. Orange, blue, and green candies: $28 \div 2 = 14$
Purple candies: $28 - 14 = 14$
green to purple = $1:2 = 7:14$
Blue candies: $7 - 1 = 6$
P(2 blue candies) $= \frac{6}{28} \times \frac{5}{27} = \frac{5}{126}$
The probability is $\frac{5}{126}$.

18. Distance: $\sqrt{52^2 + 48^2} = 70.77$
Time: $70.77 \div 1.4 = 50.55$
It takes John 50.55 seconds
to get to Tim's house.

John

48 m

Tim 52 m Ann

19. Percent increase:
$\frac{\$2.50 - \$1.99}{\$1.99} \times 100\% = 25.63\%$
Original price of popcorn:
$\$4.40 \div (1 + 25.63\%) = \$3.50$
The original price was \$3.50.

20. Amanda's time: 9:58 to 10:35 = 37 min
Amanda's speed: $25 \div 37 = 0.68$
Joe's time: 9:58 to 10:28 = 30 min
Joe's speed: $19 \div 30 = 0.63$
Amanda had a higher speed.

Unit 7

1. Store promotion:
$\$130.99 + \$130.99 \times 50\% = \$196.49$
Coupon:
$\$130.99 \times 2 \times (1 - 20\%) = \$209.58$
David should use the store promotion.

2. Girls: $30 \times 30\% = 9$
Born in Canada: $30 \times \frac{2}{3} = 20$
Boys: $30 - 9 = 21$
Not born in Canada: $30 - 20 = 10$
Girls not born in Canada: $9 - 6 = 3$
Boys not born in Canada: $10 - 3 = 7$
Probability: $\frac{7}{30}$
The probability is $\frac{7}{30}$.

3. Altitude: $a = 0.25(10) + 2.5 = 5$
$x: \sqrt{6^2 + 5^2} = 7.81$
The bird's altitude is 5 m. The value of x
is 7.81.

4. Volume of cylinder before: $\pi r^2 h$
Volume of cylinder after: $\pi(3r)^2 h = 9\pi r^2 h$
Percent increase: $\frac{9\pi r^2 h - \pi r^2 h}{\pi r^2 h} \times 100\%$
$= \frac{8\pi r^2 h}{\pi r^2 h} \times 100\%$
$= 8 \times 100\%$
$= 800\%$
The cylinder's volume will increase by 800%.

5. $6(a + 1) < 90$
$a + 1 < 15$
$a < 14$
$a^2 < 196$ ← a is the radius.
$\pi a^2 < 196 \times 3.14$
$\pi a^2 < 615.44$
The area is less than 615.44 cm².

6. 0.3 m = 30 cm
Volume of cube: $(30)^3 = 27\,000$
Volume of triangular prism:
$27\,000 \times \frac{1}{25} = 1080$
Base of triangular prism: $1080 \div 30 = 36$
Base and height of isosceles triangle:
$bh \div 2 = 36$
$b^2 = 72$
$b = 8.49$

Hypotenuse of isosceles triangle:
$\sqrt{(8.49)^2 + (8.49)^2} = 12.01$
Surface area:
$36 \times 2 + 8.49 \times 30 \times 2 + 12.01 \times 30 = 941.7$
The surface area of the triangular prism is
941.7 cm².

7. $\frac{(-3)^4}{2} = \frac{81}{2} = 40.5$ $-\sqrt{\frac{2^2}{7^0}} = -\sqrt{\frac{2^2}{1}} = -2$
$(-2 + 3)^3 = 1^3 = 1$ $(\frac{3^7}{3^2})^0 = (3^5)^0 = 1$
$(-7) \times (\frac{1^{10}}{14}) = -7 \times \frac{1}{14} = -\frac{1}{2}$
There are 2 cards that are less than 1.
Probability: $\frac{2}{5} \times \frac{1}{4} = \frac{1}{10}$
The probability is $\frac{1}{10}$.

8. Side length: $\sqrt{54 \div 6} = \sqrt{9} = 3$
Speed: $s = 7.1 \times 3 + 9 = 30.3$
The speed of the cube is 30.3 cm/s.

9. Slope: $\frac{(-2) - (3)}{1 - (-1)} = \frac{-5}{2} = -2\frac{1}{2}$
The slope is $-2\frac{1}{2}$.
(Suggested answer)
The coordinates are (1,-2).

10. Discount rate: $\frac{\$29.20 - \$20.44}{\$29.20} \times 100\% = 30\%$
Cost of lilies:
$\$19.25 \times (1 - 30\%) \times (1 + 10\%) = \$14.82$
A bouquet of lilies costs \$14.82.

11. Area of base: $12 \times 12 = 144$
Area of 1 triangular face: $(336-144) \div 4 = 48$
Height of triangular face: $48 \times 2 \div 12 = 8$
Height of pyramid: $\sqrt{8^2 - (12 \div 2)^2} = 5.29$
Volume: $\frac{1}{3} \times 12 \times 12 \times 5.29 = 253.92$
Its volume is 253.92 cm³.

12. toonies to loonies = 3:2 = 9:6
loonies to quarters = 3:1 = 6:2
toonies to loonies to quarters to total = 9:6:2:17
A total of $0.50 must be 2 quarters.
Probability: $\frac{2}{17} \times \frac{1}{16} = \frac{1}{136}$
The probability is $\frac{1}{136}$.

13. Let w be the width of the desk.
$$w \times 3w - \frac{1}{2}w \times \frac{1}{2}w \times 3 > 1$$
$$3w^2 - \frac{3}{4}w^2 > 1$$
$$2\frac{1}{4}w^2 > 1$$
$$w^2 > \frac{4}{9}$$
$$w > \frac{2}{3}$$
Area of desk: $w \times 3w > \frac{2}{3} \times 3 \times \frac{2}{3}$
$$3w^2 > 1\frac{1}{3}$$
The area of the desk is greater than $1\frac{1}{3}$ m².

14. Height after 2 s: $h = -(2)^2 + 4 \times 2 + 2 = 6$
Height after 4 s: $h = -(4)^2 + 4 \times 4 + 2 = 2$
$\frac{2}{6} \neq \frac{4}{2}$ ← time
← height
The height of the bowling pin was 6 m after 2 s and 2 m after 4 s. The time was not proportional to the height.

15. Length of track: $100 \times 2 + 3.14 \times 50 = 357$
Time per lap for Joseph: $357 \div 1.4 = 255$
Speed of Adam: $1.4 + 0.1 = 1.5$
Time per lap for Adam: $357 \div 1.5 = 238$
LCM of 238 and 255: 3570
They will meet again at the flag after 3570 seconds.

16. By angles in a triangle:
$8y - 20 + 3y + 6(y + 5) = 180$
$8y - 20 + 3y + 6y + 30 = 180$
$17y = 170$
$y = 10$
By angles in a triangle:
$16x - 6 + 5x + 5(x + 6) = 180$
$16x - 6 + 5x + 5x + 30 = 180$
$26x = 156$
$x = 6$
$3y = 30$ $8y - 20 = 60$ $6(y + 5) = 90$
$5x = 30$ $5(x + 6) = 60$ $16x - 6 = 90$
Yes, the triangles are congruent by ASA.

17. Side length of square: $\sqrt{196} = 14$
Area of 1 semicircle:
$3.14 \times (14 \div 2)^2 \div 2 = 76.93$
Total area: $196 + 76.93 \times 4 = 503.72$
Percent of square:
$196 \div 503.72 \times 100\% = 38.91\%$
The square takes up 38.91% of the total area.

18. Slope: $\frac{1 - (-4)}{1 - (-3)} = \frac{5}{4}$
Distance:
$\sqrt{4^2 + 5^2} \times 1 = 6.4$
The slope of his dive was $\frac{5}{4}$. He travelled 6.4 m.

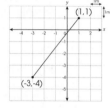

19. Let r be the radius of the cylinder.
$3.14 \times r^2 \times 3r = 1177.5$
$9.42r^3 = 1177.5$
$r^3 = 125$
$r = 5$
Surface area:
$2 \times 3.14 \times 5^2 + 2 \times 3.14 \times 5 \times 5 \times 3 = 628$
Its surface area is 628 cm².

20. By angles in the triangle:
$a + 5\sqrt{a^2} + a + 4a - 18 = 180$
$a + 5a + a + 4a - 18 = 180$
$11a = 198$
$a = 18$
$4a - 18 = 4 \times 18 - 18 = 54$
$5\sqrt{a^2} + a = 5 \times \sqrt{18^2} + 18 = 108$
By corresponding angles: $\angle BCD = 48°$
Not all the angles within the fields are the same.
No, Field ABC and Field DBC are not congruent.

Unit 8

1. By angles in a triangle:
$5x + 10x + 3(x + 6) = 180$
$5x + 10x + 3x + 18 = 180$
$18x = 162$
$x = 9$
$5x = 45$ $10x = 90$ $3(x + 6) = 45$
The triangle is a right isosceles triangle.
Let s be the base and height of the triangle.
$s^2 + s^2 = \sqrt{50}^2$
$2s^2 = 50$
$s^2 = 25$
$s = 5$
Perimeter: $5 + 5 + \sqrt{50} = 17.07$
No, she is incorrect. The perimeter is 17.07 cm.

ISBN: 978-1-77149-206-5

2. Radius: $2 \times 3.14 \times r \times 20 = 376.8$
$125.6r = 376.8$
$r = 3$
Volume: $3.14 \times 3^2 \times 20 = 565.2$
The volume of the roller is 565.2 cm³.

3. Hypotenuse of each triangle: $\sqrt{2^2 + 3^2} = 3.61$
Perimeter: $3.61 + 3.61 + 2 + 2 + 3 + 3 = 17.22$
The perimeter of $\triangle ABC$ is 17.22 m.

4. Radius of small pizza: $3.14 \times r^2 > 452.16$
$r^2 > 144$
$r > 12$
Ratio: $2:3 = 12:18$
Circumference of big pizza:
$r > 18$
$2\pi r > 2 \times 3.14 \times 18$
$2\pi r > 113.04$
The circumference is greater than 113.04 cm.

5. Let p be the profit.
$p > (3600 + 1400) \times 55\%$
$p > 2750$
$\frac{4}{5}p > 2750 \times \frac{4}{5}$
$\frac{4}{5}p > 2200$
The down payment was more than $2200.

6. Distance: $\sqrt{2.8^2 + 5.1^2} = 5.82$
No. of leaps: $5.82 \div 0.97 = 6$
The grasshopper will have to make 6 leaps.

7. cars to houses = $4:3 = 8:6$
houses to coins = $2:5 = 6:15$
cars to houses to coins to total = $8:6:15:29$
$(8+6+15)$
Probability: $\frac{6}{29} \times \frac{5}{28} = \frac{15}{406}$
The probability is $\frac{15}{406}$.

8. x-coordinate: $4 - 6 = -2$
New coordinates: $(-2, y)$
Slope: $-\frac{2}{3} = \frac{y - (-3)}{(-2) - 4}$
$-\frac{2}{3} = \frac{y + 3}{-6}$
$4 = y + 3$
$1 = y$
The y-coordinate is 1.

9. Radius of cone: $40 \div 2 = 20$
Volume of cone:
$\frac{1}{3} \times 3.14 \times 20^2 \times 60 = 25\,120$
Volume of box: $40 \times 40 \times 60 = 96\,000$
Percent: $25\,120 \div 96\,000 \times 100\% = 26.17\%$
The volume of the cone is 25 120 cm³. It takes up 26.17% of the box.

10. Height: $8.635x^2 \div (3.14 \times (\frac{x}{2})^2)$
$= 8.635x^2 \div 0.785x^2 = 11$
Total volume:
$3.14 \times (1.5x)^2 \times 11 = 77.715x^2$
Volume of toilet paper:
$77.715x^2 - 8.635x^2 = 69.08x^2$
The volume of the toilet paper is $69.08x^2$.

11. Height: $5 + 3 = 8$ $\qquad$ Width: $8 \times 50\% = 4$
Surface area:
$4 \times 5 \times 2 + 4 \times 8 \times 2 + 5 \times 8 \times 2 = 184$
The surface area is 184 cm².

12. Height: $x^2 \div 2 = 33.62$
$x^2 = 67.24$
$x = 8.2$
Hypotenuse: $\sqrt{8.2^2 + 8.2^2} = 11.6$
Its height is 8.2 cm and its
hypotenuse is 11.6 cm.

13. white to black = $2:1 = 4:2$ $\qquad$ (4+2+1)
white to black to green to total = $4:2:1:7$
Probability: P(2 white) + P(2 black)
$= \frac{4}{7} \times \frac{3}{6} + \frac{2}{7} \times \frac{1}{6} = \frac{2}{7} + \frac{1}{21} = \frac{1}{3}$
The probability is $\frac{1}{3}$.

14. Each angle in an equilateral triangle is 60°.
By supplementary angles:
$x = 180° - \frac{60°}{2} - 73° = 77°$

By angles in a triangle: $y = 180° - 90° - 77° = 13°$
Half the length of board: $\sqrt{50^2 + 150^2} = 158.11$
Length of board: $158.11 \times 2 = 316.22$
The resting board makes a 13° angle with the ground. The length is 316.22 cm.

15. Radius: $\frac{4}{3}\pi r^3 = 36\pi$
$r^3 = 27$
$r = 3$
Surface area: $4 \times 3.14 \times 3^2 = 113.04$
The surface area is 113.04 cm².

16. Total no. of residents: $96 \div \frac{72°}{360°} = 480$
Residents from 0 to 40 years old:
$480 \times \frac{150°}{360°} = 200$
There are 200 residents.

17. Let w be the no. of residents who go to work.
$200 - 2w - w > 35$
$-3w > -165$
$w < 55$
Fewer than 55 residents from 0 to 40 years old go to work.

18. Volume: $3.14 \times (25 \div 2)^2 \times 50 = 24\,531.25$
Time needed: $24\,531.25 \div 205 = 119.66$
It takes about 119.66 s to fill up the pail.

ISBN: 978-1-77149-206-5

19. Slope: $\dfrac{5-5}{2-(-2)} = \dfrac{0}{4} = 0$
    The slope of the line is 0.

20. $y = \dfrac{\sqrt{4}\,x^3}{x^2} + \dfrac{3\sqrt{b^2}}{b}$

    $y = \dfrac{2x^3}{x^2} + \dfrac{3b}{b}$

    $y = 2x + 3$

x	y
2	7
-1	1
-4	-5

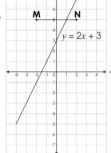

Yes, she is correct.
The relation intersects $\overline{MN}$ at (1,5).

Unit 9

1. To get a positive product when one of the cards is negative, the other card must also be negative.
   No. of negative cards: $56 \times \dfrac{3}{8} = 21$

   Probability: $\dfrac{21}{56} \times \dfrac{20}{55} = \dfrac{3}{22}$

   The probability is $\dfrac{3}{22}$.

2. Let p be the amount Juliet paid.
   $p \times (1 + 75\%) \times (1 + 12\%) + 4.96 = 63.76$
   $\qquad\qquad p \times 1.75 \times 1.12 = 58.8$
   $\qquad\qquad\qquad\qquad\qquad p = 30$
   Juliet bought the watch for $30.

3. Let b be the base and height of the triangle.
   $b^2 \div 2 = 2.5$
   $\qquad b^2 = 5$
   $\qquad\; b = \sqrt{5}$
   Hypotenuse: $\sqrt{\sqrt{5}^2 + \sqrt{5}^2} = \sqrt{10}$
   Radius: $\sqrt{10} \div 2 = \dfrac{\sqrt{10}}{2}$
   Area of rug: $3.14 \times \left(\dfrac{\sqrt{10}}{2}\right)^2 = 7.85$
   The area of the rug is 7.85 m².

4. Amount of water: $30 \times 40 \times 20 = 24\,000$
   Volume of cylinder: $3.14 \times 20^2 \times 20 = 25\,120$
   Percent filled: $24\,000 \div 25\,120 \times 100\% = 95.54\%$
   95.54% of the cylinder will be filled.

5. Side length: $s^2 + s^2 = 14^2$
   $\qquad\qquad\quad 2s^2 = 196$
   area of 1 face → $s^2 = 98$
   Surface area: $98 \times 6 = 588$
   The surface area of the cube is 588 cm².

6.

y = x		y = -x - 2		y = x - 6	
x	y	x	y	x	y
4	4	5	-7	5	-1
0	0	0	-2	0	-6
-4	-4	-4	2	-3	-9

$\sqrt{3^2 + 3^2} \times 12 = 50.91$
The length of $\overline{MN}$ is 50.91 cm.

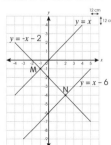

7. By opposite angles: $a = 90°$
   By alternate angles: $b = 37°$
   By angles in a triangle:
   $c = 180° - 90° - 37° = 53°$
   H: $\sqrt{12^2 + 9^2} = 15$
   B: $\sqrt{7.5^2 - 6^2} = 4.5$
   Length of wire: $12 + 9 + 15 + 6 + 7.5 + 4.5 = 54$
   The angles of the big triangle are 90°, 37°, and 53°. The length of the wire is 54 cm.

8. Since there was no mode before, at least one of the new tests had a score of 86%.
   Let x be the other new test score.
   $(83.5 \times 8 + 86 + x) \div 10 > 85$
   $\qquad\quad 668 + 86 + x > 850$
   $\qquad\qquad\qquad\qquad x > 96$
   Freddie got 86% and more than 96% on the last 2 tests.

9. Radius: $10 \div 2 = 5$
   Ratio: $2:5:3:10 = 6:15:9:30$
   Difference in height: $15 - 6 = 9$
   Difference in volume: $3.14 \times 5^2 \times 9 = 706.5$
   The volume of the biggest cylinder is 706.5 cm³ greater than the smallest one.

10. Length of slanted side:
    $\sqrt{1^2 + 4^2} \times 5 = 20.62$
    Perimeter:
    $5 \times 5 \times 2 + 20.62 \times 2 = 91.24$
    The quadrilateral is a parallelogram and its perimeter is 91.24 cm.

11. Translated point: (-4,-5)
    Slope: $\dfrac{-5 - (-5)}{3 - (-4)} = \dfrac{0}{7} = 0$
    The slope of the line of reflection is 0.

12. $24\text{ L} = 24\,000\text{ cm}^3$
    Let h be the height of the container.
    $h \times \dfrac{1}{2}h \times 150\% \times \dfrac{1}{2}h \geq 24\,000$
    $\qquad\qquad\qquad 0.375h^3 \geq 24\,000$
    $\qquad\qquad\qquad\qquad h^3 \geq 64\,000$
    $\qquad\qquad\qquad\qquad\; h \geq 40$
    The minimum height will be 40 cm.

13. $\dfrac{\sqrt{64\pi^2 r^4}}{2} = \dfrac{8\pi r^2}{2} = 4\pi r^2$
    Yes, the formula will yield the correct answer.
    $4 \times 3.14 \times r^2 \geq 113.04$
    $\qquad\qquad\quad r^2 \geq 9$
    $\qquad\qquad\qquad r \geq 3$
    Its radius is at least 3 cm.

14. Joseph's distance: $878 \times 1\dfrac{1}{2} = 1317$
    Benjamin's distance: $726 \times 2 = 1452$
    Distance between Joseph and Benjamin:
    $\sqrt{1317^2 + 1452^2} = 1960.3$
    Their destinations were 1960.3 km apart.

ISBN: 978-1-77149-206-5

15. Length of 1 lap: $3.14 \times 20 = 62.8$
Difference in speed: $4 - 3.2 = 0.8$
Time to outrun 1 lap: $62.8 \div 0.8 = 78.5$
It will take Wendy 78.5 s to outrun Derek by 1 lap.

16. No. of quarters: $\$16 \div \$0.25 = 64$
Dimes: $64 \times \dfrac{3}{4} = 48$
nickels to dimes = $5:8 = 30:48$
Total: $\$0.05 \times 30 + \$0.10 \times 48 + \$16 = \$22.30$
Geoff has $22.30 in total.

17. 2 items: $0.8 \times 2^2 + 0.5 \times 2 - 14.8 = -10.6$
20 items: $0.8 \times 20^2 + 0.5 \times 20 - 14.8 = 315.2$
Inequality: $0.8n^2 + 0.5n - 14.8 > 0$
They will make -$10.60 after selling 2 items and $315.20 after selling 20 items. The inequality is $0.8n^2 + 0.5n - 14.8 > 0$.

18. By consecutive interior angles:
$a = 180° - 90° = 90°$
By supplementary angles:
$g = 180° - 90° = 90°$
By opposite angles: $c = 46°$
Yes, there is a pair of congruent triangles that have right angles.
$\triangle$MNO and $\triangle$QPO are congruent by ASA.

19. No. of marbles in basket: $\dfrac{x}{6} = \dfrac{50}{1.5}$
$1.5x = 300$
$x = 200$
Green marbles: $200 \times \dfrac{1}{4} = 50$
Red marbles: $200 \times 31\% = 62$
Blue marbles: $200 - 50 - 62 = 88$
Probability: $\dfrac{88}{200} \times \dfrac{50}{199} = \dfrac{22}{199}$
The probability is $\dfrac{22}{199}$.

20. Ratio: $1:3:2:6 = 2.5:7.5:5:15$
The lengths of the triangle are 2.5 cm, 7.5 cm, and 5 cm.
Maverick is incorrect. The ratio of the sides are the same, but the exact lengths are not necessarily the same. The triangles are similar but not necessarily congruent.

Unit 10

1. $1\dfrac{2}{5}$ min = 84 s
Water in tank: $10 \times 84 = 840\,(mL) = 840\,(cm^3)$
Water level: $840 \div (3.14 \times 10^2) = 2.68$
The water level is 2.68 cm.

2. Buying 12 bags in-store will get 16 bags.
In-store: $\$3.99 \times 12 = \$47.88$
Online: $\$3.99 \times 16 \times (1 - 20\%) + \$5 = \$56.07$
Mary should buy the candies in-store.

3. By angles in a triangle:
$a + 90° + (115° - 90°) = 180°$
$a = 65°$
Long hypotenuse: $\sqrt{1^2 + 2.2^2} = 2.42$
Short hypotenuse: $\sqrt{(2.2 - 1)^2 + (2 - 1.5)^2} = 1.3$
Perimeter: $1.5 + 1 + 2 + 2.42 + 1 + 1.3 = 9.22$
The measure of Angle a is 65°. The perimeter is 9.22 m.

4. Side length of base: $\sqrt{625} = 25$
Height of triangular faces:
$\sqrt{(25 \div 2)^2 + 82^2} = 82.95$
Surface area: $625 + 25 \times 82.95 \div 2 \times 4$
$= 4772.5\,(cm^2) = 0.48\,(m^2)$
Cost: $\$8.55 \times 0.48 = \$4.10$
The plywood will cost $4.10.

5. $\dfrac{20.1 - 18.5}{18.5} \times 100\% = 8.65\%$
Robert's mean had improved by 8.65%.

6. $3.14 \times 2^2 \times h = \dfrac{4}{3} \times 3.14 \times 2^3$
$h = \dfrac{4}{3} \times 2$
$h = 2\dfrac{2}{3}$
The height of the cylinder was $2\dfrac{2}{3}$ cm.

7. Loonies are golden coins and dimes and quarters are silver coins.
loonies to dimes and quarters = $1:9 = 2:18$
loonies to quarters to dimes to total amount
$= 2:3:15:\$4.25 = 6:9:45:\$12.75$
$\$1 \times 2 + \$0.25 \times 3 + \$0.10 \times 15$
Total coins: $6 + 9 + 45 = 60$
Total silver coins: $9 + 45 = 54$
Probability: $\dfrac{54}{60} \times \dfrac{53}{59} = \dfrac{477}{590}$
The probability is $\dfrac{477}{590}$.

8. Length of lap: $2.5 \times 32 = 80$
$\dfrac{2}{3}$ min = 40 s
Let b be Gary's speed with backstroke.
$40 < 80 \div b$
$b < 2$
It was less than 2 m/s.

9. $2^2 = 4$ $\qquad$ $3^0 = 1$
$(\dfrac{1}{3})^{-1} = 3$ $\qquad$ $\sqrt{4} = 2$
+8 requires +4 and +4.
P(picking "+" and spinning "4"):
$\dfrac{2}{4} \times \dfrac{1}{4} = \dfrac{1}{8}$
P(picking "+" and spinning "4" for 2 rounds):
$\dfrac{1}{8} \times \dfrac{1}{8} = \dfrac{1}{64}$
The probability is $\dfrac{1}{64}$.

ISBN: 978-1-77149-206-5

10. A
   In the graph, c is 25 when f is 77.
   The temperature was 25°C.

11. New temperature: $\sqrt{25} \div 2 = 5 \div 2 = 2.5$
   Percent change: $\dfrac{25 - 2.5}{25} \times 100\% = 90\%$
   The temperature has dropped 90%.

12. $a + 16 + \dfrac{3}{2}a + \dfrac{3}{2}a = 180$ (angles in a triangle)

   $4a + 16 = 180$
   $4a = 164$
   $a = 41$
   $a + 16 = 57°$ $\dfrac{3}{2}a = 61.5°$
   By alternate angles: $b = \dfrac{3}{2}a = 61.5°$
   By angles in a triangle: $c + 61.5° + 90° = 180°$
   $c = 28.5°$
   Base of isosceles triangle: $25.9 \times 2 \div 7 = 7.4$
   Hypotenuse: $\sqrt{(7.4 \div 2)^2 + 7^2} = 7.92$
   Perimeter: $7.4 + 7.92 \times 2 = 23.24$
   The angles in the isosceles triangle are
   57°, 61.5°, and 61.5°. The angles in the
   right triangle are 90°, 61.5°, and 28.5°.
   The perimeter of the isosceles triangle is
   23.24 cm.

13.
   $180° - 56° = 124°$ (consecutive interior angles)

   Possible triangles:

   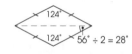
   $124° \div 2 = 62°$ $56° \div 2 = 28°$

   The triangles are congruent by SSS.
   Yes, Justin is correct. The angles in the
   triangles are either 56°, 62°, and 62° or
   124°, 28°, and 28°.

14. Let s be the side length of the square.
   $s^2 + s^2 = 19.8^2$
   $2s^2 = 392.04$
   $s^2 = 196.02$
   $s = 14$
   Radius of each coaster: $14 \div 2 \div 2 = 3.5$
   Area of each coaster: $3.14 \times 3.5^2 = 38.465$
   The area of each coaster is 38.465 cm².

15. $1:2:2:3:8 = 45:90:90:135:360$
   ↑
   sum of angles in a quadrilateral
   The angles are 45°, 90°, 90°, and 135°.
   Possible quadrilaterals with 2 right angles:
   (Suggested drawings)

   trapezoid   kite

   It could be a trapezoid or a kite.

16. Juice drunk: $0.175 \times 7 + \dfrac{1}{5} \times 7 = 2.625$
   Initial: $2.625 \div (100\% - 12.5\%) = 3$
   3 L of juice was in the carton initially.

17. Angle of phone only:
   $360° - 90° - 130° - 27° = 113°$
   Percent of phones:
   $\dfrac{130° + 113°}{360°} \times 100\% = 67.5\%$
   No. of phones: $320 \times 67.5\% = 216$
   Let d be the no. of students without data
   plans.
   $d + \dfrac{1}{5}d = 216$
   $1\dfrac{1}{5}d = 216$
   $d = 180$
   216 students own phones. 180 of them do
   not have data plans.

18. 602.9 mL $= 602.9$ cm³
   $h = d + d \times 50\% = 2r + 2r \times 50\% = 3r$
   $3.14 \times r^2 \times 3r < 602.9$
   $9.42r^3 < 602.9$
   $r^3 < 64$
   $r < 4$
   Surface area: $2\pi r^2 + 2\pi rh = 2\pi r^2 + 2\pi r(3r)$
   $= 2\pi r^2 + 6\pi r^2 = 8\pi r^2$
   $r < 4$
   $8\pi r^2 < 8 \times 3.14 \times 4^2$
   $8\pi r^2 < 401.92$
   The maximum radius is less than 4 cm and
   the maximum surface area is less than
   401.92 cm².

19. $\sqrt{x^2y^2} = xy$ $(xy)^{-1} = \dfrac{1}{xy}$
   $\dfrac{2xy}{\sqrt{4}} = \dfrac{2xy}{2} = xy$ $\dfrac{x^3yz}{x^2} = xyz$
   $(xyz)^0 = 1$ $x + y$
   Two of the cards, $\sqrt{x^2y^2}$ and $\dfrac{2xy}{\sqrt{4}}$, are equal.
   $P(\sqrt{x^2y^2}$ and then $\dfrac{2xy}{\sqrt{4}})$: $\dfrac{1}{6} \times \dfrac{1}{5} = \dfrac{1}{30}$
   $P(\dfrac{2xy}{\sqrt{4}}$ and then $\sqrt{x^2y^2})$: $\dfrac{1}{6} \times \dfrac{1}{5} = \dfrac{1}{30}$
   $P(\text{winning})$: $\dfrac{1}{30} + \dfrac{1}{30} = \dfrac{1}{15}$
   The probability is $\dfrac{1}{15}$.

20. Length of longer side:
   $\sqrt{4^2 + 1^2} \times 5 = 20.62$
   Perimeter:
   $5 \times 3 \times 2 + 20.62 \times 2 = 71.24$
   The perimeter is 71.24 cm.

   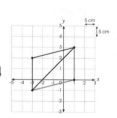

ISBN: 978-1-77149-206-5